It's another great book from CGP...

OK, so GCSE Maths can be seriously challenging — and the latest exams are tougher than ever. But help is at hand...

This life-saving CGP book is totally up-to-date for the new GCSE course. It's packed with no-nonsense explanations, plus worked examples, grade info and exam-style practice questions for every topic.

It even includes a free Online Edition to read on your computer or tablet!

How to get your free Online Edition

Just go to **cgpbooks.co.uk/extras** and enter this code...

4123 8431 4978 1214

By the way, this code only works for one person. If somebody else has used this book before you, they might have already claimed the Online Edition.

CGP — still the best! ☺

Our sole aim here at CGP is to produce the highest quality books — carefully written, immaculately presented and dangerously close to being funny.

Then we work our socks off to get them out to you — at the cheapest possible prices.

Contents

Throughout this book you'll see grade stamps like these: (3) (5) (1) (4)
You can use these to focus your revision on easier or harder work.
But remember — to get a top grade you have to know **everything**, not just the hardest topics.

Published by CGP

Written by Richard Parsons

Updated by: Rob Harrison, Shaun Harrogate, Sarah Oxley, Alison Palin, Caley Simpson

With thanks to Alastair Duncombe and Simon Little for the proofreading

Printed by Elanders Ltd, Newcastle upon Tyne.
Clipart from Corel®

Types of Number and BODMAS

Ah, the glorious world of GCSE Maths. OK maybe it's more like whiffy socks at times, but learn it you must. Here are some handy definitions of different types of number, and a bit about what order to do things in.

Integers (2)

An <u>integer</u> is another name for a <u>whole number</u> — either a positive or negative number, or zero.

<u>Examples</u>

Integers:	–365, 0, 1, 17, 989, 1 234 567 890
Not integers:	0.5, $\frac{2}{3}$, $\sqrt{7}$, $13\frac{3}{4}$, –1000.1, 66.66, π

Square and Cube Numbers (2)

1) When you <u>multiply</u> a whole number by <u>itself</u>, you get a <u>square number</u>:

1^2	2^2	3^2	4^2	5^2	6^2	7^2	8^2	9^2	10^2	11^2	12^2	13^2	14^2	15^2
1	4	9	16	25	36	49	64	81	100	121	144	169	196	225

(1×1) (2×2) (3×3) (4×4) (5×5) (6×6) (7×7) (8×8) (9×9) (10×10) (11×11) (12×12) (13×13) (14×14) (15×15)

2) When you <u>multiply</u> a whole number by <u>itself</u>, then by itself <u>again</u>, you get a <u>cube number</u>:

1^3	2^3	3^3	4^3	5^3	10^3
1	8	27	64	125	1000

(1×1×1) (2×2×2) (3×3×3) (4×4×4) (5×5×5) (10×10×10)

3) You should know these basic squares and cubes <u>by heart</u> — they could come up on a non-calculator paper, so it'll save you time if you already know what they are.

BODMAS   Brackets, Other, Division, Multiplication, Addition, Subtraction (2)

BODMAS tells you the <u>ORDER</u> in which these operations should be done:
Work out <u>Brackets</u> first, then <u>Other</u> things like squaring, then <u>Divide</u> / <u>Multiply</u> groups of numbers before <u>Adding</u> or <u>Subtracting</u> them.

EXAMPLE: Find the reciprocal of $\sqrt{4 + 6 \times (12 - 2)}$.

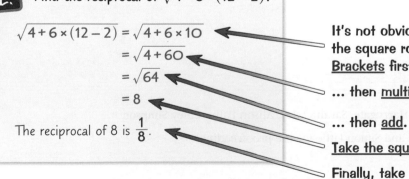

$$\sqrt{4 + 6 \times (12 - 2)} = \sqrt{4 + 6 \times 10}$$
$$= \sqrt{4 + 60}$$
$$= \sqrt{64}$$
$$= 8$$

The reciprocal of 8 is $\frac{1}{8}$.

It's not obvious what to do inside the square root — so use BODMAS. <u>Brackets</u> first...

... then <u>multiply</u>...

... then <u>add</u>.

<u>Take the square root</u>

Finally, take the <u>reciprocal</u> (the reciprocal of a number is just 1 ÷ the number).

What's your BODMAS? About 50 kg, dude...

It's really important to check your working on BODMAS questions. You might be certain you did it right, but it's surprisingly easy to make a slip. Try this Exam Practice Question and see how you do.

Q1   Without using a calculator, find the value of 3 + 22 × 3 – 14.   [2 marks] (2)

Wordy Real-Life Problems

Wordy questions can be a bit off-putting — for these you don't just have to do the maths, you've got to work out what the question's asking you to do. It's really important that you begin by reading through the question really carefully...

Don't Be Scared of Wordy Questions

Relax and work through them step by step:

> 1) READ the question carefully. Work out what bit of maths you need to answer it.
> 2) Underline the INFORMATION YOU NEED to answer the question — you might not have to use all the numbers they give you.
> 3) Write out the question IN MATHS and answer it, showing all your working clearly.

 **EXAMPLES:**

1. A return car journey from Carlisle to Manchester uses $\frac{4}{7}$ of a tank of petrol. It costs £56 for a full tank of petrol. How much does the journey cost?

You want to know $\frac{4}{7}$ of £56, so in maths: $\frac{4}{7} \times £56 = £32$

See p.12-13 for more on using fractions.

Don't forget the units in your final answer — this is a question about cost in pounds, so the units will be £.

2. A water company has two different price plans for water usage:

PLAN A	PLAN B
No fixed cost	Fixed cost of £12
23p per unit	Plus 11p per unit

A household uses 102 units of water in one month. Which price plan would be cheaper for this household in that particular month?

Cost with plan A: $102 \times £0.23 = £23.46$

Cost with plan B: $£12 + (102 \times £0.11) = £23.22$

So for this household in that particular month, plan B would be cheaper.

3. Ben buys dog food in boxes of 20 packets. Each box costs £12.50. He has 3 dogs which each eat 2 packets per day. How much will it cost Ben to buy enough boxes of food for all of his dogs for 4 weeks?

Number of packets for 3 dogs for 1 day = $3 \times 2 = 6$

Number of packets for 3 dogs for 4 weeks = $6 \times 7 \times 4 = 168$

Number of boxes needed = $168 \div 20 = 8.4$ Ben can't buy part of a box, so he needs to buy 9 boxes.

$9 \times £12.50 = £112.50$

I can cross 'wordy questions' off my list of 'Things I'm Scared Of'...

I'm still left with spiders, heights, the dark... A lot of these wordy questions have a few stages to the working — if you take them one step at a time, they're really not bad at all. Have a go at this particularly lovely Exam Practice Question.

Q1   Hank owns a fruit stall. He sells 11 apples and 5 oranges for £2.71. One apple costs 16p. How much does one orange cost?   [4 marks]

Multiplying and Dividing by 10, 100, etc.

You need to know the stuff on this page — it's <u>nice 'n' simple</u>, and they're likely to <u>test you on it</u> in the exam.

1) Multiplying and Dividing Any Number by 10

Multiply
Move the decimal point <u>ONE</u> place <u>BIGGER</u> and if it's needed, <u>ADD A ZERO</u> on the end.

E.g. 23.6 × 10 = 2 3 6

Divide
Move the decimal point <u>ONE</u> place <u>SMALLER</u> and if it's needed, <u>REMOVE ZEROS</u> after the decimal point.

E.g. 23.6 ÷ 10 = 2 . 3 6

2) Multiplying and Dividing Any Number by 100

Multiply
Move the decimal point <u>TWO</u> places <u>BIGGER</u> and <u>ADD ZEROS</u> if necessary.

E.g. 34 × 100 = 3 4 0 0

Divide
Move the decimal point <u>TWO</u> places <u>SMALLER</u> and <u>REMOVE ZEROS</u> after the decimal point.

E.g. 340 ÷ 100 = 3 . 4

3) Multiplying and Dividing by 1000 or 10 000

Multiply
Move the decimal point so many places <u>BIGGER</u> and <u>ADD ZEROS</u> if necessary.

Divide
Move the decimal point so many places <u>SMALLER</u> and <u>REMOVE ZEROS</u> after the decimal point.

You always <u>move</u> the <u>DECIMAL POINT</u> this much:
<u>1 place for 10</u>,   <u>2 places for 100</u>,
<u>3 places for 1000</u>,   <u>4 places for 10 000</u>,   etc.

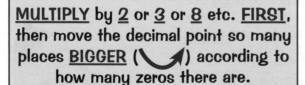

4) Multiply and Divide by Numbers like 20, 300, etc.

<u>MULTIPLY</u> by <u>2</u> or <u>3</u> or <u>8</u> etc. <u>FIRST</u>, then move the decimal point so many places <u>BIGGER</u> ( ) according to how many zeros there are.

<u>DIVIDE</u> by <u>4</u> or <u>3</u> or <u>7</u> etc. <u>FIRST</u>, then move the decimal point so many places <u>SMALLER</u> (i.e. to the left).

EXAMPLES:

1. Calculate 234 × 200.

234 × 2 = 468
468 × 100 = 46800

2. Calculate 960 ÷ 300.

960 ÷ 3 = 320
320 ÷ 100 = 3.2

Adding zeros when they're not needed? Tut, tut, noughty, noughty...

Learn the methods on this page — nothing too strenuous. For a bit of a workout, try these:

Q1   Work out   a) 12.3 × 100   b) 3.08 ÷ 1000   c) 360 ÷ 30   [3 marks]

Multiplying and Dividing Whole Numbers

You need to be really happy doing multiplications and divisions <u>without</u> a calculator
— they're likely to come up in your <u>non-calculator</u> exam.

Multiplying Whole Numbers

The Traditional Method:
1) Split it into <u>separate multiplications</u>.
2) Add up the results in <u>columns</u> (right to left).

There are lots of other multiplication methods — make sure you're comfortable using whichever method you prefer.

EXAMPLES:

1. Work out 46 × 27

```
      4 6
    × 2 7
    3 3₄2 2 ——— This is 7 × 46
    9₁2 0 ——— This is 20 × 46
  1 2 4 2 ——— This is 322 + 920
```

2. Work out 243 × 18

```
      2 4 3
    ×   1 8
  1 9₃4₂4 ——— This is 8 × 243
  2 4 3 0 ——— This is 10 × 243
  4₁3 7 4 ——— This is 1944 + 2430
```

Dividing Whole Numbers

EXAMPLE: What is 748 ÷ 22?

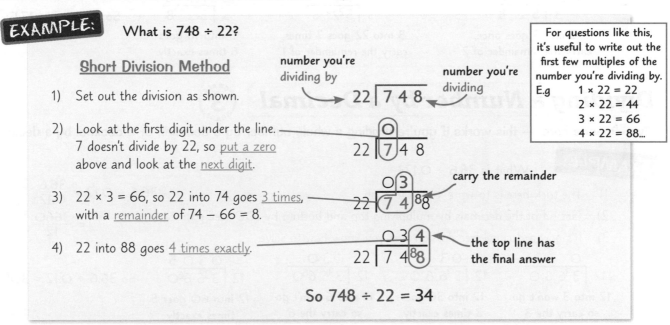

Short Division Method

1) Set out the division as shown. → 22 | 7 4 8

   number you're dividing by ← 22 | 7 4 8 → *number you're dividing*

2) Look at the first digit under the line. 7 doesn't divide by 22, so <u>put a zero</u> above and look at the <u>next digit</u>.

   22 | 7 4 8 → 0 / 22 |7|4 8

3) 22 × 3 = 66, so 22 into 74 goes <u>3 times</u>, with a <u>remainder</u> of 74 − 66 = 8.   *carry the remainder*

   22 | 7 4|⁸8 → 0 3

4) 22 into 88 goes <u>4 times exactly</u>.   *the top line has the final answer*

   22 | 7 4|⁸8 → 0 3 4

So 748 ÷ 22 = 34

For questions like this, it's useful to write out the first few multiples of the number you're dividing by.
E.g
1 × 22 = 22
2 × 22 = 44
3 × 22 = 66
4 × 22 = 88...

The other common method for dividing is <u>long division</u> — if you prefer this method, make sure you know it <u>really</u> well, so you'll have no problems with any division in your exam.

Pah, calculators? Who needs 'em...

There are lots of methods you can use for multiplication — and they all work just as well as each other. It comes down to which method you find easiest to use. Have a go at these practice questions without using a calculator — if you really know your methods, they'll be an absolute doddle. Seriously.

Q1   Work out   a) 28 × 12   b) 56 × 11   c) 104 × 16   [6 marks]

Q2   Work out   a) 96 ÷ 8   b) 84 ÷ 7   c) 252 ÷ 12   [4 marks]

Q3   Joey has a plank of wood which is 220 cm long.
     He cuts it into 14 cm pieces. What length of wood will he have left over?   [2 marks]

Multiplying and Dividing with Decimals

You might get a scary non-calculator question on multiplying or dividing using decimals. Luckily, these aren't really any harder than the whole-number versions. You just need to know what to do in each case.

Multiplying Decimals

1) Start by <u>ignoring</u> the decimal points.
   Do the multiplication using <u>whole numbers</u>.

2) Count the <u>total</u> number of digits after the <u>decimal points</u> in the original numbers.

3) Make the answer have the <u>same number</u> of decimal places.

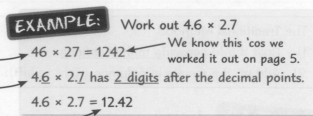

EXAMPLE: Work out 4.6 × 2.7

46 × 27 = 1242 ← We know this 'cos we worked it out on page 5.

4.<u>6</u> × 2.<u>7</u> has <u>2 digits</u> after the decimal points.

4.6 × 2.7 = 12.42

Dividing a Decimal by a Whole Number

For these, you just set the question out like a whole-number division <u>but</u> put the <u>decimal point</u> in the answer <u>right above</u> the one in the question.

EXAMPLE: What is 52.8 ÷ 3?

Put the decimal point in the answer above the one in the question.

$$3\overline{)5^2 2\ .\ 8}$$ = 1 .

3 into 5 goes once,
carry the remainder of 2.

$$3\overline{)5^2 2\ .^1 8}$$ = 1 7 .

3 into 22 goes 7 times,
carry the remainder of 1.

$$3\overline{)5^2 2\ .^1 8}$$ = 1 7 . 6

3 into 18 goes
6 times exactly.

So 52.8 ÷ 3 = 17.6

Dividing a Number by a Decimal

Two-for-one here — this works if you're dividing a whole number by a decimal, or a decimal by a decimal.

EXAMPLE: What is 36.6 ÷ 0.12?

1) The trick here is to write it as a fraction:

2) Get rid of the decimals by multiplying top and bottom by 100 (see p4):

3) It's now a decimal-free division that you know how to solve:

$$36.6 \div 0.12 = \frac{36.6}{0.12}$$
$$= \frac{3660}{12}$$

$$12\overline{)3^3 6\ 6\ 0}$$ = O

12 into 3 won't go
so carry the 3

$$12\overline{)3^3 6\ 6\ 0}$$ = O 3

12 into 36 goes
3 times exactly

$$12\overline{)3^3 6\ 6^6 0}$$ = O 3 O

12 into 6 won't go
so carry the 6

$$12\overline{)3^3 6\ 6^6 0}$$ = O 3 O 5

12 into 60 goes 5
times exactly

So 36.6 ÷ 0.12 = 305

The decimals came in two by two...

Just like you did with whole-numbers on p5, use the method you prefer for multiplying or dividing. Have a go at these practice questions without using your calculator.

Q1   Work out   a) 3.2 × 56   b) 0.6 × 10.2   c) 5.5 × 10.2   [6 marks]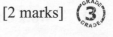

Q2   Emma buys 14 packets of biscuits for a party. Each packet of biscuits costs £1.27.
How much does Emma spend on biscuits in total?   [2 marks]

Q3   Claire has £22.38. She wants to share it equally between her three nephews.
How much does each nephew receive?   [2 marks]

Q4   Find   a) 33.6 ÷ 0.6   b) 45 ÷ 1.5   c) 84.6 ÷ 0.12   [6 marks]

Negative Numbers

Numbers less than zero are <u>negative</u>. You should be able to <u>add</u>, <u>subtract</u>, <u>multiply</u> and <u>divide</u> with them.

Adding and Subtracting with Negative Numbers

Use the <u>number line</u> for <u>addition</u> and <u>subtraction</u> involving negative numbers:

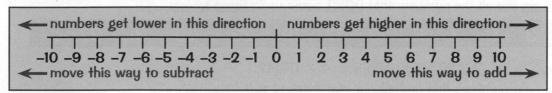

EXAMPLES:

What is −4 + 7? Start at −4 and move 7 places in the positive direction:

So −4 + 7 = 3

Work out 5 − 8 Start at 5 and move 8 places in the negative direction:

So 5 − 8 = −3

Find −2 − 4 Start at −2 and move 4 places in the negative direction:

So −2 − 4 = −6

Good evening caller, you're through to the Number Line. What's your problem?

Use These Rules for Combining Signs

```
+  +  makes  +
+  −  makes  −
−  +  makes  −
−  −  makes  +
```

These rules are <u>ONLY TO BE USED WHEN</u>:

1) <u>Multiplying or dividing</u>

EXAMPLES:

(invisible + sign)

Find: a) −2 × 3   − + makes − so −2 × 3 = −6

b) −8 ÷ −2   − − makes + so −8 ÷ −2 = 4

Be careful when squaring or cubing. <u>Squaring</u> a negative number gives a <u>positive</u> number (e.g. −2 × −2 = 4) but <u>cubing</u> a negative number gives a <u>negative</u> number (e.g. −3 × −3 × −3 = −27).

2) <u>Two signs appear next to each other</u>

EXAMPLES:

Work out: a) 5 − −4   − − makes + so 5 − −4 = 5 + 4 = 9

b) 4 + −6 − −7   + − makes − and − − makes +
so 4 + −6 − −7 = 4 − 6 + 7 = 5

Just call the Number Line on −7654321...*

Don't just learn the rules in that red box — make sure you know when you can use them too.

Q1 The temperature in Mathchester at 9 am on Monday was 4 °C.
At 9 am on Tuesday the temperature was −2 °C.
a) What was the change in temperature from Monday to Tuesday? [1 mark]
b) The temperature at 9 am on Wednesday was 3 °C lower than on Tuesday.
What was the temperature on Wednesday? [1 mark]

*Don't really. Even if your phone accepts negative numbers.

Prime Numbers

'Prime numbers?' I hear you ask. 'What are these magical things you speak of?'
Read on, my friend, and you shall see...

PRIME Numbers Don't Divide by Anything

Prime numbers are all the numbers that DON'T come up in times tables:

| 2 | 3 | 5 | 7 | 11 | 13 | 17 | 19 | 23 | 29 | 31 | 37 | ... |

The only way to get ANY PRIME NUMBER is: 1 × ITSELF

E.g.   The only numbers that multiply to give 7 are 1 × 7
The only numbers that multiply to give 31 are 1 × 31

EXAMPLE: Show that 24 is not a prime number.

Just find another way to make 24 other than 1 × 24:   2 × 12 = 24

24 divides by other numbers apart from 1 and 24, so it isn't a prime number.

Five Important Facts

1) 1 is **NOT** a prime number.
2) 2 is the **ONLY** even prime number.
3) The first four prime numbers are 2, 3, 5 and 7.
4) Prime numbers end in 1, 3, 7 or 9 (2 and 5 are the only exceptions to this rule).
5) But **NOT ALL** numbers ending in 1, 3, 7 or 9 are primes, as shown here:
(Only the circled ones are primes.)

```
②  ③  ⑤  ⑦
⑪  ⑬  ⑰  ⑲
21  ㉓  27  ㉙
㉛  33  ㊲  39
㊶  ㊸  ㊼  49
51  ㊾  57  ㊾
㉛  63  ㊲  69
```

How to FIND Prime Numbers — a very simple method

1) All primes (above 5) end in 1, 3, 7 or 9. So ignore any numbers that don't end in one of those.
2) Now, to find which of them **ACTUALLY ARE** primes you only need to divide each one by 3 and by 7. If it doesn't divide exactly by 3 or by 7 then it's a prime.

This simple rule using just 3 and 7 is true for checking primes up to 120.

EXAMPLE: Find all the prime numbers in this list: 71, 72, 73, 74, 75, 76, 77, 78

1 First, get rid of anything that doesn't end in 1, 3, 7 or 9:   71, 72, 73, 74, 75, 76, 77, 78

2 Now try dividing 71, 73 and 77 by 3 and 7:
71 ÷ 3 = 23.667   71 ÷ 7 = 10.143   so 71 is a prime number
73 ÷ 3 = 24.333   73 ÷ 7 = 10.429   so 73 is a prime number
77 ÷ 3 = 25.667   BUT: 77 ÷ 7 = 11 — 11 is a whole number,
so 77 is NOT a prime, because it divides by 7.
So the prime numbers in the list are **71** and **73**.

Two is the oddest prime of all — it's the only one that's even...

Learn all three sections above, then cover the page and try this Exam Practice Question without peeking:

Q1   Below is a list of numbers. Write down all the prime numbers from the list.
39, 51, 46, 35, 61, 53, 42, 47
[2 marks]

Multiples, Factors and Prime Factors

If you think 'factor' is short for 'fat actor', you should give this page a read. Stop thinking about fat actors.

Multiples and Factors

The MULTIPLES of a number are just its <u>times table</u>.

 EXAMPLE: Find the first 8 multiples of 13.

You just need to find the first 8 numbers in the 13 times table:
13   26   39   52   65   78   91   104

The FACTORS of a number are all the numbers that <u>divide into it</u>.

There's a method that guarantees you'll find them all:

1) Start off with 1 × the number itself, then try 2 ×, then 3 × and so on, listing the pairs in rows.
2) Try each one in turn. Cross out the row if it doesn't divide exactly.
3) Eventually, when you get a number <u>repeated</u>, <u>stop</u>.
4) The numbers in the rows you haven't crossed out make up the list of factors.

EXAMPLE: Find all the factors of 24.

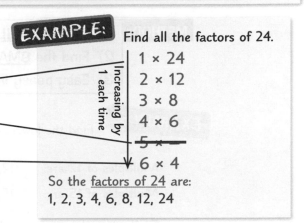

Increasing by 1 each time

1 × 24
2 × 12
3 × 8
4 × 6
5 ×
6 × 4

So the <u>factors of 24</u> are:
1, 2, 3, 4, 6, 8, 12, 24

Finding Prime Factors — The Factor Tree

<u>Any number</u> can be broken down into a string of prime numbers all multiplied together — this is called '<u>expressing it as a product of prime factors</u>', or its '<u>prime factorisation</u>'.

EXAMPLE: Express 420 as a product of prime factors.

```
        420
       /    \
      42     10
     /  \   /  \
    ⑦   6  ②   ⑤
       / \
      ②   ③
```

So 420 = 2 × 2 × 3 × 5 × 7 = 2^2 × 3 × 5 × 7

To write a number as a product of its prime factors, use the <u>Factor Tree</u> method:

1) Start with the number at the top, and <u>split</u> it into <u>factors</u> as shown.
2) Every time you get a prime, <u>ring it</u>.
3) Keep going until you can't go further (i.e. you're just left with primes), then write the primes out <u>in order</u>. If there's more than one of the <u>same factor</u>, you can write them as <u>powers</u>.

No matter which numbers you choose at each step, you'll find that the prime factorisation is exactly the same. Each number has a <u>unique</u> set of prime factors.

Takes me back, scrumping prime factors from the orchard...

Make sure you know the Factor Tree method inside out, then give these Exam Practice Questions a go...

Q1 Use the following list of numbers to answer the questions below. 4, 6, 10, 14, 15, 17, 24, 30
a) Find one number that's a multiple of 2, a multiple of 3 and a multiple of 4. [1 mark]
b) Find one number that's a multiple of 3 and a factor of 36. [2 marks]

Q2 What number should replace the ? in the equation 14 × 30 = 7 × ? to make it true? [1 mark]

Q3 Express as products of their prime factors: a) 990 [2 marks] b) 160 [2 marks]

LCM and HCF

Two big fancy names but don't be put off — they're both <u>real easy</u>. There are two methods for finding each — this page starts you off with the <u>nice</u>, <u>straightforward</u> methods.

LCM — 'Lowest Common Multiple'

'<u>Lowest Common Multiple</u>' — sure, it sounds kind of complicated, but all it means is this:

> The <u>SMALLEST</u> number that will <u>DIVIDE BY ALL</u> the numbers in question.

METHOD:
1) <u>LIST</u> the <u>MULTIPLES</u> of <u>ALL</u> the numbers.
2) Find the <u>SMALLEST</u> one that's in <u>ALL the lists</u>.
3) Easy peasy innit?

The LCM is sometimes called the Least (instead of 'Lowest') Common Multiple.

EXAMPLE: Find the lowest common multiple (LCM) of 12 and 15.

Multiples of 12 are: 12, 24, 36, 48, (60,) 72, 84, 96, ...
Multiples of 15 are: 15, 30, 45, (60,) 75, 90, 105, ...

So the <u>lowest common multiple</u> (LCM) of 12 and 15 is 60.
Told you it was easy.

HCF — 'Highest Common Factor'

'<u>Highest Common Factor</u>' — all it means is <u>this</u>:

> The <u>BIGGEST</u> number that will <u>DIVIDE INTO ALL</u> the numbers in question.

METHOD:
1) <u>LIST</u> the <u>FACTORS</u> of <u>ALL</u> the numbers.
2) Find the <u>BIGGEST</u> one that's in <u>ALL the lists</u>.
3) Easy peasy innit?

EXAMPLE: Find the highest common factor (HCF) of 36, 54, and 72.

Factors of 36 are: 1, 2, 3, 4, 6, 9, 12, (18,) 36
Factors of 54 are: 1, 2, 3, 6, 9, (18,) 27, 54
Factors of 72 are: 1, 2, 3, 4, 6, 8, 9, 12, (18,) 24, 36, 72

So the <u>highest common factor</u> (HCF) of 36, 54 and 72 is 18.
Told you it was easy.

Just <u>take care</u> listing the factors — make sure you use the <u>proper method</u> (as shown on the previous page) or you'll miss one and blow the whole thing out of the water.

LCM and HCF live together — it's a House of Commons...

You need to learn what LCM and HCF are, and how to find them. Turn over and write it all down. And after that, some lovely Exam Practice Questions — bonus.

Q1   Find the lowest common multiple (LCM) of 12, 14 and 21.   [2 marks]

Q2   Find the highest common factor (HCF) of 36 and 84.   [2 marks]

LCM and HCF

The two <u>methods</u> on this page are a <u>little trickier</u> — but you might have to use them in your exam.

LCM — Alternative Method

If you already know the <u>prime factors</u> of the numbers, you can use this method instead:

1) List all the <u>PRIME FACTORS</u> that appear in <u>EITHER</u> number.
2) If a factor appears <u>MORE THAN ONCE</u> in one of the numbers, list it <u>THAT MANY TIMES</u>.
3) <u>MULTIPLY</u> these together to give the <u>LCM</u>.

 $18 = 2 \times 3^2$ and $30 = 2 \times 3 \times 5$.
Find the LCM of 18 and 30.

$18 = 2 \times 3 \times 3$ $30 = 2 \times 3 \times 5$

So the prime factors that appear in either number are: 2, 3, 3, 5 — List 3 twice as it appears twice in 18.

LCM = $2 \times 3 \times 3 \times 5 = 90$

HCF — Alternative Method

Again, there's a different method you can use if you already know the <u>prime factors</u> of the numbers:

1) List all the <u>PRIME FACTORS</u> that appear in <u>BOTH</u> numbers.
2) <u>MULTIPLY</u> these together to find the HCF.

 $180 = 2^2 \times 3^2 \times 5$ and $84 = 2^2 \times 3 \times 7$.
Use this to find the HCF of 180 and 84.

$180 = ②\times②\times③\times 3 \times 5$ $84 = ②\times②\times③\times 7$

2, 2 and 3 are prime factors of both numbers, so
HCF = $2 \times 2 \times 3 = 12$

Real-Life LCM and HCF Questions

You might be asked a wordy real-life LCM or HCF question in your exam — these can be <u>tricky</u> to spot at first, but once you have done, the method's <u>just the same</u>.

EXAMPLE: Maggie is making party bags. She has 60 balloons, 48 lollipops and 84 stickers. She wants to use them all. Each type of item must be distributed equally between the party bags. What is the maximum number of party bags she can make?

You could use the <u>prime factorisation</u> method here if you wanted — use whichever method's <u>easier</u> for you.

Factors of 60 are: 1, 2, 3, 4, 5, 6, 10, ⑫ 15, 20, 30, 60
Factors of 48 are: 1, 2, 3, 4, 6, 8, ⑫ 16, 24, 48
Factors of 84 are: 1, 2, 3, 4, 6, 7, ⑫ 14, 21, 28, 42, 84

The <u>highest common factor</u> (HCF) of 60, 48 and 84 is 12, so the maximum number of party bags Maggie can make is 12.

So, in each bag there will be
60 ÷ 12 = 5 balloons,
48 ÷ 12 = 4 lollipops
and 84 ÷ 12 = 7 stickers.

Ain't no factor high enough, ain't no multiple low enough...

Have a go at these Exam Practice Questions to see if you've got the hang of this LCM and HCF business.

Q1 $112 = 2^4 \times 7$ and $140 = 2^2 \times 5 \times 7$. Use this to find the HCF of 112 and 140.   [1 mark]

Q2   A café sells different cakes each day. It sells banana cake every 8 days, and raspberry cake every 22 days. If the café is selling the two cakes today, how many days will it be until the cakes are both sold on the same day again?   [3 marks]

Fractions without a Calculator

These pages show you how to cope with fraction calculations without your beloved calculator.

1) Cancelling down

To cancel down or simplify a fraction, divide top and bottom by the same number, till they won't go further:

EXAMPLE: Simplify $\frac{18}{24}$.

Cancel down in a series of easy steps — keep going till the top and bottom don't have any common factors.

$$\frac{18}{24} \overset{\div 3}{\underset{\div 3}{=}} \frac{6}{8} \overset{\div 2}{\underset{\div 2}{=}} \frac{3}{4}$$

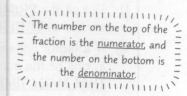
The number on the top of the fraction is the numerator, and the number on the bottom is the denominator.

2) Mixed numbers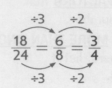

Mixed numbers are things like $3\frac{1}{3}$, with an integer part and a fraction part. Improper fractions are ones where the top number is larger than the bottom number. You need to be able to convert between the two.

EXAMPLES:

1. Write $4\frac{2}{3}$ as an improper fraction.

1) Think of the mixed number as an addition:
$$4\frac{2}{3} = 4 + \frac{2}{3}$$

2) Turn the integer part into a fraction:
$$4 + \frac{2}{3} = \frac{12}{3} + \frac{2}{3} = \frac{12+2}{3} = \frac{14}{3}$$

2. Write $\frac{31}{4}$ as a mixed number.

Divide the top number by the bottom.
1) The answer gives the whole number part.
2) The remainder goes on top of the fraction.

$$31 \div 4 = 7 \text{ remainder } 3 \quad \text{so} \quad \frac{31}{4} = 7\frac{3}{4}$$

3) Multiplying

Multiply top and bottom separately. Then simplify your fraction as far as possible.

EXAMPLE: Find $\frac{8}{5} \times \frac{7}{12}$.

Multiply the top and bottom separately:
$$\frac{8}{5} \times \frac{7}{12} = \frac{8 \times 7}{5 \times 12}$$

Then simplify — top and bottom both divide by 4.
$$= \frac{56}{60} = \frac{14}{15}$$

4) Dividing

Turn the 2nd fraction **UPSIDE DOWN** and then multiply:

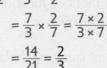
When you're multiplying or dividing with mixed numbers, always turn them into improper fractions first.

EXAMPLE: Find $2\frac{1}{3} \div 3\frac{1}{2}$.

Rewrite the mixed numbers as improper fractions:
$$2\frac{1}{3} \div 3\frac{1}{2} = \frac{7}{3} \div \frac{7}{2}$$

Turn $\frac{7}{2}$ upside down and multiply:
$$= \frac{7}{3} \times \frac{2}{7} = \frac{7 \times 2}{3 \times 7}$$

Simplify — top and bottom both divide by 7.
$$= \frac{14}{21} = \frac{2}{3}$$

Fractions without a Calculator

5) Common denominators

This comes in handy for <u>ordering fractions</u> by size, and for <u>adding</u> or <u>subtracting</u> fractions.
You need to find a number that <u>all</u> the denominators <u>divide into</u> — this will be your <u>common denominator</u>.
The simplest way is to find the <u>lowest common multiple</u> of the denominators:

EXAMPLE: Put these fractions in ascending order of size: $\frac{8}{3}, \frac{5}{4}, \frac{12}{5}$

The <u>LCM</u> of 3, 4 and 5 is 60,
so make 60 the <u>common denominator</u>:

$$\frac{8}{3} = \frac{160}{60} \quad (\times 20)$$
$$\frac{5}{4} = \frac{75}{60} \quad (\times 15)$$
$$\frac{12}{5} = \frac{144}{60} \quad (\times 12)$$

So the correct order is $\frac{75}{60}, \frac{144}{60}, \frac{160}{60}$ i.e. $\frac{5}{4}, \frac{12}{5}, \frac{8}{3}$

Don't forget to use the original fractions in the final answer.

6) Adding, subtracting — sort the denominators first

1) Make sure the denominators are <u>the same</u> (see above).
2) Add (or subtract) the top lines <u>only</u>.

If you're adding or subtracting <u>mixed numbers</u>, it usually helps to convert them to improper fractions first.

EXAMPLE: Calculate $2\frac{1}{5} - 1\frac{1}{2}$.

Rewrite the <u>mixed numbers</u> as improper <u>fractions</u>: $2\frac{1}{5} - 1\frac{1}{2} = \frac{11}{5} - \frac{3}{2}$

Find a <u>common denominator</u>: $= \frac{22}{10} - \frac{15}{10}$

Combine the <u>top lines</u>: $= \frac{22-15}{10} = \frac{7}{10}$

7) Fractions of something

EXAMPLE: What is $\frac{9}{20}$ of £360?

'$\frac{9}{20}$ of £360' means '$\frac{9}{20} \times$ £360'.
<u>Multiply</u> by the top of the fraction and <u>divide</u> by the bottom.
$\frac{9}{20} \times £360 = (£360 \div 20) \times 9$
$= £18 \times 9 = £162$

The order that you multiply and divide in doesn't matter — just start with whatever's easiest.

8) Expressing as a Fraction

EXAMPLE: Write 180 as a fraction of 80.

Write the first number over the second and <u>cancel down</u>.
$$\frac{180}{80} = \frac{9}{4}$$

No fractions were harmed in the making of these pages...

...although one was slightly frightened for a while, and several were tickled.
When you think you've learnt all this, try all of these Exam Practice Questions without a calculator.

Q1 Calculate: a) $\frac{5}{8} \times 1\frac{5}{6}$ [3 marks] b) $\frac{10}{7} \div \frac{8}{3}$ [2 marks]

c) $\frac{8}{9} + \frac{19}{27}$ [2 marks] d) $5\frac{2}{3} - 9\frac{1}{4}$ [3 marks]

Q2 Dean has made 30 sandwiches. $\frac{7}{15}$ of the sandwiches he has made are vegetarian, and $\frac{3}{7}$ of the vegetarian sandwiches are cheese sandwiches. How many cheese sandwiches has he made? [2 marks]

Fraction Problems

The previous two pages gave you all the tools you'll need to tackle these more pesky fraction questions. All these questions could come up on the non-calculator paper so put your calculators away.

Use the Methods You've Already Learnt

 **1.** Rachel is making cupcakes. Each cupcake needs $\frac{2}{25}$ of a pack of butter. How many packs of butter will Rachel need to buy to make 30 cupcakes?

Once you've done the multiplication, convert $\frac{60}{25}$ to a mixed number to see how many packs she'll need — careful though, she can only buy a whole number of packs.

1 cupcake needs $\frac{2}{25}$ of a pack of butter, so 30 cupcakes need:

$$30 \times \frac{2}{25} = \frac{60}{25} = \frac{12}{5} = 2\frac{2}{5} \text{ packs}$$

2 packs won't be enough, so Rachel will need to buy 3 packs.

2. The diamond to the right is made up of two identical equilateral triangles. The equilateral triangle at the top is split into three equal triangles. The equilateral triangle at the bottom is split into two equal triangles. Find the fraction of the diamond that is shaded.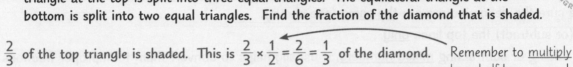

$\frac{2}{3}$ of the top triangle is shaded. This is $\frac{2}{3} \times \frac{1}{2} = \frac{2}{6} = \frac{1}{3}$ of the diamond.

$\frac{1}{2}$ of the bottom triangle is shaded. This is $\frac{1}{2} \times \frac{1}{2} = \frac{1}{4}$ of the diamond.

Find a common denominator to add the fractions. $\frac{1}{3} + \frac{1}{4} = \frac{4}{12} + \frac{3}{12} = \frac{7}{12}$

Remember to multiply by a half because each equilateral triangle makes up half the diamond.

3. Which of the fractions, $\frac{2}{3}$ or $\frac{9}{7}$, is closer to 1?

1) Give the fractions a common denominator.

$$\frac{2}{3} = \frac{2 \times 7}{3 \times 7} = \frac{14}{21} \qquad \frac{9}{7} = \frac{9 \times 3}{7 \times 3} = \frac{27}{21}$$

2) Convert 1 into a fraction and subtract to see which fraction is closer to 1.

$$\frac{21}{21} - \frac{14}{21} = \frac{7}{21} \qquad \frac{27}{21} - \frac{21}{21} = \frac{6}{21} \qquad \text{So } \frac{9}{7} \text{ is closer to 1.}$$

4. At the Prism School, year 10 is split into two classes, each with the same number of pupils in total. $\frac{3}{5}$ of one class are girls, and $\frac{4}{7}$ of the other class are girls. What fraction of year 10 students are girls?

1) Divide each fraction by 2 to find the number of girls in each class as a fraction of total year 10 pupils.

Class 1 girls are: $\frac{3}{5} \div 2 = \frac{3}{10}$ of the total pupils in Year 10.

Class 2 girls are: $\frac{4}{7} \div 2 = \frac{4}{14}$ of the total pupils in Year 10.

2) Find a common denominator, then add the fractions.

So $\frac{3}{10} + \frac{4}{14} = \frac{21}{70} + \frac{20}{70} = \frac{41}{70}$ of Year 10 pupils are girls.

I've got $\frac{99}{100}$ problems, but fractions ain't one...

OK, so fraction questions can be a little bit nasty — but get plenty of practice and they won't be so bad.

Q1 Bill has some books. They're all fiction books, biographies or history books. $\frac{3}{14}$ of the books are biographies and $\frac{1}{6}$ are history books. What fraction of Bill's books are fiction books? Give your answer as a fraction in its simplest form. **[4 marks]**

Fractions, Decimals and Percentages

Fractions, decimals and percentages are <u>three different ways</u> of describing when you've got <u>part</u> of a <u>whole thing</u>. They're <u>closely related</u> and you can <u>convert between them</u>. These tables show some really common conversions which you should know straight off without having to work them out:

Fraction	Decimal	Percentage
$\frac{1}{2}$	0.5	50%
$\frac{1}{4}$	0.25	25%
$\frac{3}{4}$	0.75	75%
$\frac{1}{3}$	0.333333...	$33\frac{1}{3}\%$
$\frac{2}{3}$	0.666666...	$66\frac{2}{3}\%$
$\frac{5}{2}$	2.5	250%

Fraction	Decimal	Percentage
$\frac{1}{10}$	0.1	10%
$\frac{2}{10}$	0.2	20%
$\frac{1}{5}$	0.2	20%
$\frac{2}{5}$	0.4	40%
$\frac{1}{8}$	0.125	12.5%
$\frac{3}{8}$	0.375	37.5%

The more of those conversions you learn, the better — but for those that you <u>don't know</u>, you must <u>also learn</u> how to <u>convert</u> between the three types. These are the methods:

$$\text{Fraction} \xrightarrow{\text{Divide}} \text{Decimal} \xrightarrow{\times \text{ by } 100} \text{Percentage}$$

E.g. $\frac{7}{20}$ is $7 \div 20$ = 0.35   e.g. 0.35×100 = 35%

$$\text{Fraction} \longleftarrow \text{Decimal} \longleftarrow \text{Percentage}$$

The awkward one $\div$ by 100

<u>Converting decimals to fractions</u> is awkward. To convert terminating decimals to fractions:

The digits after the decimal point go on the top, and a <u>10, 100, 1000, etc.</u> on the bottom — so you have the same number of zeros as there were decimal places.

$0.6 = \frac{6}{10}$ $0.78 = \frac{78}{100}$ $0.024 = \frac{24}{1000}$ etc.   These can often be <u>cancelled down</u> — see p.12.

Recurring Decimals have Repeating Digits

1) Recurring decimals have a <u>pattern of numbers</u> which <u>repeats forever</u>, e.g. 0.333333... which is $\frac{1}{3}$.

2) The <u>repeating part</u> is usually marked with <u>dots</u> on top of the number.

3) If there's <u>one dot</u>, only <u>one digit</u> is repeated. If there are <u>two dots</u>, <u>everything from the first dot to the second dot</u> is the repeating bit.

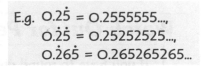

E.g. $0.2\dot{5} = 0.2555555...,$
$0.\dot{2}\dot{5} = 0.25252525...,$
$0.\dot{2}6\dot{5} = 0.265265265...$

4) You can <u>convert</u> a fraction to a recurring decimal:

EXAMPLE: Write $\frac{5}{11}$ as a recurring decimal.

Just do the division, and look for the <u>repeating pattern</u>. $5 \div 11 = 0.454545...$ so $\frac{5}{11} = 0.\dot{4}\dot{5}$

Eight out of ten cats prefer the perfume Eighty Purr Scent...

Learn the top tables and the conversion processes. Then it's time to break into a mild sweat...

Q1   Which is greater: a) 57% or $\frac{5}{9}$,   b) 0.2 or $\frac{6}{25}$,   c) $\frac{7}{8}$ or 90%?   [3 marks]

Q2   a) Write 0.555 as a fraction in its simplest form.   [2 marks]

       b) Write $\frac{1}{6}$ as a recurring decimal.   [2 marks]

Rounding Numbers

You need to be able to use <u>3 different rounding methods</u>.
We'll do decimal places first, but there's the same basic idea behind all three.

Decimal Places (d.p.)

To round to a given number of <u>decimal places</u>:

1 <u>Identify</u> the position of the 'last digit' from the number of decimal places.

2 Then look at the next digit to the <u>right</u> — called <u>the decider</u>.

3 If the <u>decider</u> is <u>5 or more</u>, then <u>round up</u> the <u>last digit</u>.
If the <u>decider</u> is <u>4 or less</u>, then leave the <u>last digit</u> as it is.

4 There must be <u>no more digits</u> after the last digit (not even zeros).

> If you're rounding to <u>2 d.p.</u> the last digit is the <u>second</u> digit after the decimal point.

EXAMPLES:

1. What is 13.72 correct to <u>1 decimal place</u>?

$$13.\boxed{7}\boxed{2} = 13.7$$

<u>LAST DIGIT</u> to be written (1st decimal place because we're rounding to 1 d.p.)

<u>DECIDER</u>

The <u>LAST DIGIT</u> stays the <u>same</u> because the <u>DECIDER</u> is <u>4 or less</u>.

2. What is 7.45839 to <u>2 decimal places</u>?

$$7.4\boxed{5}\boxed{8}39 = 7.46$$

<u>LAST DIGIT</u> to be written (2nd decimal place because we're rounding to 2 d.p.)

<u>DECIDER</u>

The <u>LAST DIGIT</u> rounds <u>UP</u> because the <u>DECIDER</u> is <u>5 or more</u>.

Watch Out for Pesky Nines

If you have to <u>round up</u> a <u>9</u> (to 10), replace the 9 with 0, and <u>add 1</u> to the digit on the <u>left</u>.

E.g. Round 45.698 to 2 d.p.:   45.698 $\longrightarrow$ 45.69 (→ 45.70) $\longrightarrow$ 45.70 to 2 d.p.

last digit — round up

The question asks for 2 d.p. so you <u>must</u> put 45.<u>70</u> not 45.7.

Well, I think that's put those decimals in their place...

This is important stuff, so learn the steps of the basic method and then have a crack at these:

Q1 a) Give 21.435 correct to 1 decimal place
   b) Give 0.0581 correct to 2 d.p.
   c) Round 4.968 to 1 d.p.   [3 marks]

Q2 Calculate $\dfrac{25.49 - 16.73}{2.82}$

and give your answer to 2 d.p.   [2 marks]

Rounding Numbers

Significant Figures (s.f.)

The 1st significant figure of any number is the first digit which isn't a zero.

The 2nd, 3rd, 4th, etc. significant figures follow immediately after the 1st — they're allowed to be zeros.

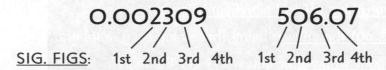

0.002309   506.07

SIG. FIGS: 1st 2nd 3rd 4th   1st 2nd 3rd 4th

To round to a given number of significant figures:

1) Find the last digit — if you're rounding to, say 3 s.f., then the 3rd significant figure is the last digit.

2) Use the digit to the right of it as the decider, just like for d.p.

3) Once you've rounded, fill up with zeros, up to but not beyond the decimal point.

EXAMPLE: Round 506.07 to 2 significant figures.

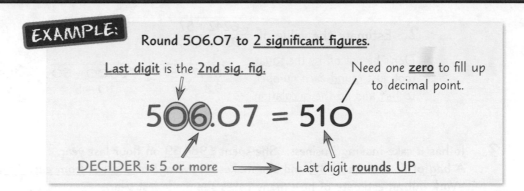

Last digit is the 2nd sig. fig.

Need one zero to fill up to decimal point.

506.07 = 510

DECIDER is 5 or more ⟶ Last digit rounds UP

To the Nearest Whole Number, Ten, Hundred etc.

You might be asked to round to the nearest whole number, ten, hundred, thousand, or million:

1) Identify the last digit, e.g. for the nearest whole number it's the units position, and for the 'nearest ten' it's the tens position, etc.

2) Round the last digit and fill in with zeros up to the decimal point, just like for significant figures.

EXAMPLE: Round 6751 to the nearest hundred.

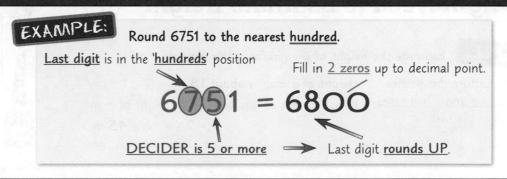

Last digit is in the 'hundreds' position

Fill in 2 zeros up to decimal point.

6751 = 6800

DECIDER is 5 or more ⟶ Last digit rounds UP.

Julius Caesar, Henry VIII, Einstein — all significant figures...

Now, learn the whole of this page, turn over and write down everything you've learned. And for pudding...

Q1 a) Round 653 to 1 s.f.   b) Round 14.6 to 2 s.f.
    c) Give 168.7 to the nearest whole number.
    d) Give 82 430 to the nearest thousand.   [4 marks]

Q2 Calculate $\frac{8.43 + 12.72}{5.63 - 1.21}$.
    Give your answer to 2 s.f.   [2 marks]

Estimating

'Estimate' doesn't mean 'take a wild guess', it means 'look at the numbers, make them a bit easier, then do the calculation'. Your answer won't be as <u>accurate</u> as the real thing but hey, it's easier on your brain.

Estimating Calculations

① <u>Round everything off</u> to <u>1 significant figure</u>.

② Then <u>work out the answer</u> using these nice easy numbers.

③ <u>Show all your working</u> or you won't get the marks.

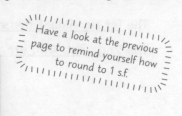
Have a look at the previous page to remind yourself how to round to 1 s.f.

EXAMPLES:

1. Estimate the value of 42.6 × 12.1.

$\approx$ means 'approximately equal to'.

1) <u>Round</u> each number to <u>1 s.f.</u>   42.6 × 12.1 $\approx$ 40 × 10

2) Do the <u>calculation</u> with the rounded numbers.   = 400

You might have to say if it's an <u>underestimate</u> or an <u>overestimate</u>. Here, you rounded both numbers <u>down</u>, so it's an <u>underestimate</u>.

2. Estimate the value of $\dfrac{\sqrt{6242 \div 57}}{9.8 - 4.7}$.

Don't be put off by the <u>square root</u>, just <u>round</u> each number to 1 s.f and do the <u>calculation</u>.

$$\frac{\sqrt{6242 \div 57}}{9.8 - 4.7} \approx \frac{\sqrt{6000 \div 60}}{10 - 5} = \frac{\sqrt{100}}{5} = \frac{10}{5} = 2$$

3. Jo has a cake-making business. She spent <u>£984.69</u> on flour last year. A bag of flour costs <u>£1.89</u>, and she makes an average of <u>5 cakes from each bag</u> of flour. Work out an estimate of how many cakes she made last year.

1) Estimate number of bags of flour — <u>round</u> numbers to <u>1 s.f.</u>

Number of bags of flour = $\dfrac{984.69}{1.89}$

$$\approx \frac{1000}{2} = 500$$

Don't panic if you get a <u>'real-life'</u> estimating question — just round everything to 1 s.f. as before.

2) Multiply to find the number of cakes.

Number of cakes $\approx$ 500 × 5 = 2500

You Might Need to Estimate Height

EXAMPLE: Estimate the height of the giraffe in the picture.

In the picture the giraffe's about <u>two and a half times</u> as tall as the man.

Height of a man is about 1.8 m

Rough height of giraffe = 2.5 × height of man

= 2.5 × 1.8 = 4.5 m

Use <u>1.8 m</u> as an estimate for the <u>height of a man</u>.

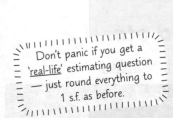

And he definitely said Tim ate the calculation? How odd...

If you're asked to estimate something in the exam, make sure you show all your steps (including what each number is rounded to) to prove that you didn't just use a calculator. That would be naughty.

Q1   Estimate the value of: a) $\dfrac{22.3 \times 11.4}{0.532}$ [2 marks] ④   b) $\sqrt{\dfrac{18.79 \times 5.22}{1.23 + 3.21}}$ [2 marks] ④

Q2   Kate buys 17 kg of turnips at a cost of £1.93 per kg. Estimate the total cost.   [2 marks] ④

Rounding Errors

Whenever a number is <u>rounded</u> or <u>truncated</u> it will have some amount of <u>error</u>.
The error tells you how far the <u>actual value</u> could be away from the <u>rounded value</u>.

Rounded Measurements Can Be Out By Half A Unit

> Whenever a measurement is <u>rounded off</u> to a <u>given UNIT</u> the
> <u>actual measurement</u> can be anything up to <u>HALF A UNIT bigger or smaller</u>.

I. A room is measured to be <u>9 m long</u> to the <u>nearest metre</u>.
What are its minimum and maximum possible lengths?

The measurement is to the <u>nearest 1 m</u>,
so the actual length could be
<u>up to 0.5 m bigger or smaller</u>.

Minimum length = 9 − 0.5 = 8.5 m
Maximum length = 9 + 0.5 = 9.5 m

The <u>actual</u> maximum length is 9.4999... m, but it's OK to say 9.5 m instead.

If you're asked for the <u>error interval</u>, you can use <u>inequalities</u> to show the actual maximum:

2. The mass of a cake is given as 2.4 kg to the nearest 0.1 kg.
Find the interval within which m, the actual mass of the cake, lies.

Minimum mass = 2.4 − 0.05 = <u>2.35</u> kg
Maximum mass = 2.4 + 0.05 = <u>2.45</u> kg

So the interval is 2.35 kg ≤ m < 2.45 kg

See p.37 for more on inequalities.

The actual value is <u>greater than or equal to</u> the <u>minimum</u> but <u>strictly less than</u> the <u>maximum</u>.
The actual mass of the cake could be <u>exactly</u> 2.35 kg,
but if it was exactly 2.45 kg it would <u>round up</u> to 2.5 kg instead.

Truncated Measurements Can Be A Whole Unit Out

You truncate a number by <u>chopping off</u> decimal places. E.g. 25.765674 truncated to 1 d.p. would be 25.7

> When a measurement is <u>**TRUNCATED**</u> to a <u>given UNIT</u>, the <u>actual</u>
> <u>measurement</u> can be up to <u>A WHOLE UNIT bigger but no smaller</u>.

If the mass of the cake in example 2 was 2.4 kg <u>truncated</u> to 1 d.p.
the error interval would be 2.4 kg ≤ m < 2.5 kg.
So even if the mass was 2.499999 kg, it would still truncate to 2.4 kg.

Don't underestimate the need to eat biscuits when revising...

You need to be comfortable with rounding before you tackle this topic — so if you're feeling a bit
unsure, take a look back at those pages. Feeling confident? Then have a go at these questions now.

Q1 James has an apple with a mass of 138 g to the nearest gram.
What is the minimum possible mass of the apple? [1 mark]

Q2 The following numbers have been rounded to 2 significant figures.
Give the error interval for each: a) 380 [2 marks] b) 0.46 [2 marks]

Powers

You've already seen 'to the power 2' and 'to the power 3' — they're just 'squared' and 'cubed'.
They're just the tip of the iceberg — any number can be a power if it puts its mind to it...

Powers are a very Useful Shorthand

① Powers are 'numbers <u>multiplied by themselves</u> so many times':

$$2 \times 2 \times 2 \times 2 \times 2 \times 2 \times 2 = 2^7 \text{ ('two to the power 7')}$$

② The <u>powers of ten</u> are really easy — the power tells you the number of zeros:

$$10^1 = 10 \qquad 10^2 = 100 \qquad 10^3 = 1000 \qquad 10^6 = 1\,000\,000$$

to the power of 6 ← → 6 zeros

③ Use the $x^\blacksquare$ or y^x button on your calculator to find powers,

e.g. press 3 . 7 $x^\blacksquare$ 3 = to get $3.7^3 = 50.653$.

④ Anything to the <u>power 1</u> is just <u>itself</u>, e.g. $4^1 = 4$.

⑤ <u>1 to any power</u> is <u>still 1</u>, e.g. $1^{457} = 1$.

⑥ <u>Anything</u> to the <u>power 0</u> is just <u>1</u>, e.g. $5^0 = 1$, $67^0 = 1$, $x^0 = 1$.

Four Easy Rules:

1) When **MULTIPLYING**, you **ADD THE POWERS**. e.g. $3^4 \times 3^6 = 3^{4+6} = 3^{10}$

2) When **DIVIDING**, you **SUBTRACT THE POWERS**. e.g. $c^4 \div c^2 = c^{4-2} = c^2$

3) When **RAISING** one power to another, you **MULTIPLY THE POWERS**. e.g. $(3^2)^4 = 3^{2 \times 4} = 3^8$

4) **FRACTIONS** — Apply the power to <u>both TOP and BOTTOM</u>. e.g. $\left(\frac{2}{3}\right)^3 = \frac{2^3}{3^3} = \frac{8}{27}$

> <u>Warning</u>: Rules 1 & 2 <u>don't work</u> for things like $2^3 \times 3^7$, only for <u>powers of the same number</u>.

EXAMPLE: $a = 5^9$ and $b = 5^4 \times 5^2$. What is the value of $\frac{a}{b}$?

1) Work out b — <u>add</u> the powers: $b = 5^4 \times 5^2 = 5^{4+2} = 5^6$

2) <u>Divide</u> a by b — <u>subtract</u> the powers: $\frac{a}{b} = 5^9 \div 5^6 = 5^{9-6} = 5^3 = 125$

One Trickier Rule

To find a <u>negative power</u> — turn it <u>upside-down</u>.

People have real difficulty remembering this — whenever you see a <u>negative power</u> you need to immediately think: "Aha, that means turn it the other way up and make the power positive".

E.g. $7^{-2} = \frac{1}{7^2} = \frac{1}{49}$, $\left(\frac{3}{5}\right)^{-2} = \left(\frac{5}{3}\right)^2 = \frac{5^2}{3^2} = \frac{25}{9}$

"I've got the power! oh, oh, oh..." Oh no, I'm feeling kinda 90s...

Learn this page off by heart, then cover it up and have a go at these...

Q1 a) Find $3^3 + 4^2$ without a calculator.
b) Use your calculator to find 6.2^3.
c) Write ten thousand as a power of 10.
  [4 marks]

Q2 Simplify: a) $4^2 \times 4^3$ b) $\frac{7^6}{7^3}$ c) $(q^2)^4$ [3 marks]

Q3 Without using a calculator, find:
a) $\frac{6^3 \times 6^5}{6^6}$ b) 2^{-4} [4 marks]

Roots

Take a deep breath, and get ready to tackle this page. Good luck with it, I'll be rootin' for ya...

Square Roots

'Squared' means 'multiplied by itself': $8^2 = 8 \times 8 = 64$

SQUARE ROOT $\sqrt{\ }$ is the reverse process: $\sqrt{64} = 8$

> 'Square Root' means 'What Number Times by Itself gives...'

EXAMPLES:

1. What is $\sqrt{49}$?

7 times by itself gives 49: $49 = 7 \times 7$

So $\sqrt{49} = 7$

> 49 is a square number — make sure you know all the square numbers on p2 so you can answer questions like this without a calculator.

2. What is $\sqrt{29.16}$?

Use your calculator. Press:  5.4

3. Find both square roots of 36.

$6 \times 6 = 36$, so positive square root = 6

$-6 \times -6 = 36$, so negative square root = -6

> All numbers also have a NEGATIVE SQUARE ROOT — it's just the '–' version of the normal positive one.

This little rule for multiplying roots might come in handy in your exam:

$$\sqrt{a} \times \sqrt{a} = a$$

> Be careful — this is only true if you're multiplying together two roots which are the same.

Cube Roots

'Cubed' means 'multiplied by itself and then by itself again': $2^3 = 2 \times 2 \times 2 = 8$

CUBE ROOT $\sqrt[3]{\ }$ is the reverse process: $\sqrt[3]{8} = 2$

> 'Cube Root' means 'What Number Times by Itself and then by Itself Again gives...'

You need to be able to write down the cube roots of the cube numbers given on p2 without a calculator. To find the cube root of any other number you can use your calculator — press $\sqrt[3]{\ }$.

EXAMPLES:

1. What is $\sqrt[3]{27}$?

> 27 is a cube number.

3 times by itself and then by itself again gives 27:

$27 = 3 \times 3 \times 3$

So $\sqrt[3]{27} = 3$

2. What is $\sqrt[3]{4913}$?

Press: 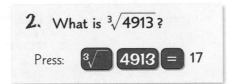 17

> Make sure you know how to use your calculator to find higher order roots — the buttons might be slightly different to these ones.

You can use your calculator to find any root of a number, using the $\sqrt[x]{\ }$ or $\sqrt[\square]{\square}$ buttons.

"Cue brute", that's what I call Charley when I play him at snooker...

Once you've got the meanings of square root and cube root well and truly sorted, have a go at these.

Q1 Find a) $\sqrt{196}$ without using a calculator. b) $\sqrt[3]{9261}$ c) $\sqrt[7]{2187}$ [3 marks]

Q2 The volume of a cube is 1.728 cm³. Find the length of one of its sides, in cm. [2 marks]

Q3 Work out $\sqrt[3]{19.34} + (1.3 + 2.5)^2$. Write down the full calculator display. [1 mark]

Standard Form

Standard form is useful for writing <u>VERY BIG</u> or <u>VERY SMALL</u> numbers in a more convenient way.

E.g.   56 000 000 000 would be 5.6×10^{10} in standard form.

0.000 000 003 45 would be 3.45×10^{-9} in standard form.

But <u>ANY NUMBER</u> can be written in standard form and you need to know how to do it:

What it Actually is:

A number written in standard form must <u>always</u> be in <u>exactly</u> this form:

This <u>number</u> must <u>always</u> be <u>between 1 and 10</u>.

(The fancy way of saying this is $1 \le A < 10$)

$$A \times 10^n$$

This number is just the <u>number of places</u> the <u>decimal point</u> moves.

Learn the Three Rules:

1) The <u>front number</u> must always be <u>between 1 and 10</u>.

2) The power of 10, n, is <u>how far the decimal point moves</u>.

3) n is <u>positive for BIG numbers</u>, n is <u>negative for SMALL numbers</u>.

(This is much better than rules based on which way the decimal point moves.)

Four Important Examples:

 Express 35 600 in standard form.

1) <u>Move the decimal point</u> until 35 600 becomes 3.56 ($1 \le A < 10$)

2) The decimal point has moved <u>4 places</u> so n = 4, giving: 10^4

3) 35 600 is a <u>big number</u> so n is +4, not −4

$$3.5\,6\,0\,0$$
$$= 3.56 \times 10^4$$

---

2 **Express 0.0000623 in standard form.**

1) The decimal point must move <u>5 places</u> to give 6.23 ($1 \le A < 10$). So the power of 10 is 5.

2) Since 0.0000623 is a <u>small number</u> it must be 10^{-5} not 10^{+5}

$$0.0\,0\,0\,0\,6\,23$$
$$= 6.23 \times 10^{-5}$$

---

3 **Express 4.95×10^{-3} as an ordinary number.**

1) The power of 10 is <u>negative</u>, so it's a <u>small number</u> — the answer will be less than 1.

2) The power is −3, so the decimal point moves <u>3 places</u>.

$$0\,0\,0\,4.9\,5 \times 10^{-3}$$
$$= 0.00495$$

---

4 **Which is the largest number in the following list?** 9.5×10^8 2.7×10^5 3.6×10^8 5.6×10^6

1) Compare the <u>powers</u> first.

9.5×10^8 and 3.6×10^8 have the biggest powers so one of them is the largest.

2) Then, compare the <u>front numbers</u>.

9.5 is greater than 3.6 So 9.5×10^8 is the largest number.

Standard Form

You might be asked to add, subtract, multiply or divide using numbers in standard form <u>without</u> using a calculator.

Multiplying and Dividing

1) Rearrange to put the <u>front numbers</u> and the <u>powers of 10 together</u>.
2) Multiply or divide the front numbers, and use the <u>power rules</u> (see p.20) to multiply or divide the powers of 10.
3) Make sure your answer is still in <u>standard form</u>.

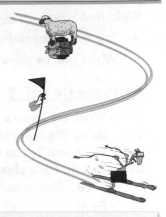

EXAMPLES:

1. Find $(2 \times 10^3) \times (6 \times 10^5)$ without using a calculator. Give your answer in standard form.

$(2 \times 10^3) \times (6 \times 10^5)$

Multiply front numbers and powers separately
$= (2 \times 6) \times (10^3 \times 10^5)$

$= 12 \times 10^{3+5}$ —— Add the powers (see p.20)

$= 12 \times 10^8$

Not in standard form so convert it — divide the number by 10...
$= 1.2 \times 10^9$ —— ... and multiply the power by 10.

2. Calculate $(2 \times 10^5) \div (4 \times 10^{10})$ without using a calculator. Give your answer in standard form.

$(2 \times 10^5) \div (4 \times 10^{10})$

Divide front numbers and powers separately
$= \dfrac{2 \times 10^5}{4 \times 10^{10}} = \dfrac{2}{4} \times \dfrac{10^5}{10^{10}}$

$= 0.5 \times 10^{5-10}$ —— Subtract the powers (see p.20)

Not in standard form so convert it — multiply the number by 10...
$= 0.5 \times 10^{-5}$

$= 5 \times 10^{-6}$ —— ... and divide the power by 10.

Adding and Subtracting

1) Make sure the <u>powers of 10</u> are <u>the same</u>.
2) Add or subtract the <u>front numbers</u>.
3) Convert the answer to <u>standard form</u> if necessary.

EXAMPLE: Calculate $(2.8 \times 10^4) + (6.6 \times 10^4)$ without using a calculator. Give your answer in standard form.

1) <u>Check</u> that both powers of 10 are equal. $(2.8 \times 10^4) + (6.6 \times 10^4)$
2) Then add the <u>front numbers</u>: $= (2.8 + 6.6) \times 10^4$
3) This is in standard form, so you <u>don't</u> need to convert it: $= 9.4 \times 10^4$

To put standard form numbers into your <u>calculator</u>, use the [EXP] or the [×10ˣ] button. E.g. enter 2.67×10^{15} by pressing [2.67] [EXP] [15] [=] or [2.67] [×10ˣ] [15] [=] .

Or for just £25, you can upgrade to luxury form...

Make sure you understand all the examples on these pages. Then answer these Exam Practice Questions:

Q1 Write a) 4.32×10^8 as an ordinary number. [1 mark] (4)
       b) 0.000387 in standard form. [1 mark]

Q2 Which of these numbers is the smallest? 2.6×10^{-3} 1.9×10^{-3} 3.4×10^{-2} [1 mark] (4)

Q3 Work out the following. Give your answers in standard form.
       a) $(9 \times 10^7) \div (3 \times 10^4)$ [3 marks]   b) $(6.7 \times 10^{10}) - (4.8 \times 10^{10})$ [2 marks] (5)

Revision Questions for Section One

Well, that wraps up <u>Section One</u> — time to put yourself to the test and find out <u>how much you really know</u>.

- Try these questions and <u>tick off each one</u> when you <u>get it right</u>.
- When you've done <u>all the questions</u> for a topic and are <u>completely happy</u> with it, tick off the topic.

Arithmetic (p2-7) ☐

Calculators are <u>only allowed</u> in questions 2, 7, 9, 10, 15 and 22. Sorry.

1) What are square numbers? Write down the first ten of them. ☑
2) Using the numbers 2, 4 and 5, and +, −, × and ÷, what is the smallest possible positive number you can make? You can use each number/operation a maximum of once. You may also use brackets. ☑
3) Tickets for a show cost £12 each. A senior's ticket is half price. A child's ticket is a third of the full price. How much does it cost for a family of 2 adults, 2 children and 1 senior to watch the show? ☑
4) Find: a) £1.20 × 100 b) £150 ÷ 300 ☑
5) Work out: a) 51 × 27 b) 338 ÷ 13 c) 3.3 × 19 d) 4.2 ÷ 12 ☑
6) Find: a) −10 − 6 b) −35 ÷ −5 c) −4 + −5 + 22 − −7 ☑

Primes, Factors and Multiples (p8-11) ☐

7) Find all the prime numbers between 40 and 60 (there are 5 of them). ☑
8) What are multiples? Find the first six multiples of: a) 10 b) 4 ☑
9) Express each of these as a product of prime factors: a) 210 b) 1050 ☑
10) Find: a) the HCF of 42 and 28 b) the LCM of 8 and 10 ☑

Fractions and Decimals (p12-15) ☑

11) Work out without a calculator: a) $\frac{25}{6} \div \frac{8}{3}$ b) $\frac{2}{3} \times 4\frac{2}{5}$ c) $\frac{5}{8} + \frac{9}{4}$ d) $\frac{2}{3} - \frac{1}{7}$ ☑
12) Calculate a) $\frac{4}{7}$ of 560 b) $\frac{2}{5}$ of £150 ☑
13) Amy, Brad and Cameron are all playing a video game. Amy has completed $\frac{5}{8}$ of the game, Brad has completed $\frac{7}{11}$ of the game and Cameron has completed $\frac{15}{22}$ of the game. Who has the largest fraction of the game left to complete? ☑
14) Write: a) 0.04 as: (i) a fraction (ii) a percentage b) 65% as: (i) a fraction (ii) a decimal ☑
15) a) What is a recurring decimal? b) Write $\frac{2}{9}$ as a recurring decimal. ☑

Rounding and Estimating (p16-19) ☑

16) Round: a) 17.65 to 1 d.p. b) 6743 to 2 s.f. c) 3 643 510 to the nearest million. ☑
17) Estimate the value of a) $\frac{17.8 \times 32.3}{6.4}$ b) $\frac{96.2 \times 7.3}{0.463}$ ☑
18) Give the error intervals for the following: a) a number that is 200 when rounded to 1 s.f.
   b) a number that is 24.6 when truncated to 1 d.p. ☑

Powers and Roots (p20-21) ☑

19) If $f = 7^6 \times 7^4$ and $g = 7^5$, what is $f \div g$? ☑
20) What is the value of 5^{-2}? Give your answer as a fraction. ☑
21) Find without using a calculator: a) $\sqrt{121}$ b) $\sqrt[3]{64}$ c) $8^2 - 2^3$ d) 100 000 as a power of ten. ☑
22) Use a calculator to find: a) 7.5^3 b) $\sqrt{23.04}$ c) $\sqrt[3]{512}$ d) $\sqrt[5]{161051}$ ☑

Standard Form (p22-23) ☑

23) What are the three rules for writing numbers in standard form? ☑
24) Write: a) 3 560 000 000 in standard form b) 2.75×10^{-6} as an ordinary number. ☑
25) Calculate: a) $(3.2 \times 10^6) \div (1.6 \times 10^3)$ b) $(5 \times 10^{11}) + (7 \times 10^{11})$
   Give your answers in standard form. ☑

Algebra — Simplifying

Algebra really terrifies so many people. But honestly, it's not that bad.
Make sure you <u>understand and learn</u> these <u>basics</u> for dealing with algebraic expressions.

Terms

Before you can do anything else with algebra, you must understand what a <u>term</u> is:

> **A TERM IS A COLLECTION OF NUMBERS, LETTERS AND BRACKETS,
> ALL MULTIPLIED/DIVIDED TOGETHER**

Terms are separated by <u>+ and − signs</u>. Every term has a + or − attached to the <u>front of it</u>.

If there's no sign in front of the first term, it means there's an invisible + sign.

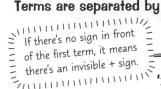 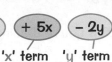 

$4x^2$ $+ 5x$ $- 2y$ $+ 6y^2$ $+ 4$

'x^2' term   'x' term   'y' term   'y^2' term   'number' term

Simplifying or 'Collecting Like Terms' ②

To <u>simplify</u> an algebraic expression made up of all the <u>same terms</u>, just <u>add</u> or <u>subtract</u> them.

EXAMPLES:

1. Simplify $q + q + q + q + q$

Just <u>add up</u> all the q's:

$q + q + q + q + q = 5q$

'q' just means '1q'.

2. Simplify $4t + 5t - 2t$

Again, just <u>combine the terms</u> — don't forget there's a '−' before the 2t:

$4t + 5t - 2t = 7t$

If you have a mixture of <u>different terms</u>, it's a bit more tricky. To <u>simplify</u> an algebraic expression like this, you combine '<u>like terms</u>' (e.g. all the x terms, all the y terms, all the number terms etc.).

EXAMPLE:

Simplify $2x - 4 + 5x + 6$

number terms

Invisible + sign $(2x)$ (-4) $(+5x)$ $(+6)$ $=$ $(2x)$ $(+5x)$ (-4) $(+6)$ $= 7x + 2$

       x-terms $7x$ $+2$

1) Put <u>bubbles</u> round each term — be sure you capture the <u>+/− sign</u> in front of each.
2) Then you can move the bubbles into the <u>best order</u> so that <u>like terms</u> are together.
3) <u>Combine like terms</u>.

EXAMPLE:

Simplify $4 + \sqrt{3} - 1 + 3\sqrt{3}$

Don't be put off by the $\sqrt{3}$-terms. Just treat them like x-terms — don't combine them with the number terms.

$\sqrt{3}$-terms

Invisible + sign (4) $(+\sqrt{3})$ (-1) $(+3\sqrt{3})$ $=$ (4) (-1) $(+\sqrt{3})$ $(+3\sqrt{3})$ $= 3 + 4\sqrt{3}$

       number-terms 3 $+4\sqrt{3}$

Collecting like terms — less exciting than collecting stamps...

Q1   Simplify: a) $2a + 7a + 4a$ [1 mark] ②   b) $6b + 8b - 3b - b$ [1 mark] ②

Q2   Simplify: a) $5x + y - 2x + 7y$ [1 mark] ②   b) $6 + 5\sqrt{5} + 3 - 2\sqrt{5}$ [2 marks]

Algebra — Multiplying and Dividing

Multiplying algebra is a lot like multiplying numbers — here are a few rules to get you started.

Multiplying and Dividing Letters

Watch out for these combinations of letters in algebra that regularly catch people out:

1) abc means a × b × c and 3a means 3 × a. The ×'s are often left out to make it clearer.

2) gn^2 means g × n × n. Note that only the n is squared, not the g as well.

3) $(gn)^2$ means g × g × n × n. The brackets mean that BOTH letters are squared.

4) Powers tell you how many letters are multiplied together — so $r^6 = r \times r \times r \times r \times r \times r$.

5) $\frac{a}{b}$ means a ÷ b. Use the power rules from p.20 if you're dividing powers of the same letter.

EXAMPLES:

1. Simplify k × k × k × k
You have 4 k's multiplied together:
$k \times k \times k \times k = k^4$

Careful — k times itself 4 times is k^4, not 4k (4k means k + k + k + k or 4 × k).

2. Simplify 2p × 3q × 5
Multiply the numbers together, then the letters together:
$2p \times 3q \times 5 = 2 \times 3 \times 5 \times p \times q = 30pq$

3. Simplify $6m^2 ÷ 8m$
Write as a fraction then simplify: $6m^2 ÷ 8m = \frac{6m^2}{8m} = \frac{3}{4}m$

$m^2 ÷ m = m$

Leave the number in front of the letter as a fraction not a decimal

Multiplying Brackets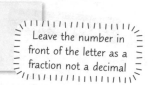

The key thing to remember about multiplying brackets is that the thing outside the brackets multiplies each separate term inside the brackets.

EXAMPLE: Expand the following:

a) 3(2x + 5)
= (3 × 2x) + (3 × 5)
= 6x + 15

b) −4(3y − 2)
= (−4 × 3y) + (−4 × −2)
= −12y + 8

c) 2e(e − 4)
= (2e × e) + (2e × −4)
= $2e^2 − 8e$

EXAMPLE: Expand $x(2x + 1) + y(y − 4) + 3x(y + 2)$

1) Expand each bracket separately.
$x(2x + 1) + y(y − 4) + 3x(y + 2)$
$= 2x^2 + x + y^2 − 4y + 3xy + 6x$

2) Group together like terms.
$= 2x^2 + x + 6x + 3xy + y^2 − 4y$

3) Simplify the expression.
$= 2x^2 + 7x + 3xy + y^2 − 4y$

Ahhh algebra — it's as easy as abc...

There's lots to take in here — hopefully a bit of practice on these questions will help you out.

Q1 Simplify: a) $5r \times −2s \times 6$ [1 mark]   b) 7(3m − 2) [1 mark]   c) 4p(p + 2q) [1 mark]

Q2 Show that 5(x + 8) + 2(x − 12) = 7x + 16. [2 marks]

Multiplying Double Brackets

<u>Double</u> brackets are a bit more tricky than single brackets — this time, you have to multiply <u>everything</u> in the <u>first bracket</u> by <u>everything</u> in the <u>second bracket</u>.

Use the FOIL Method to Multiply Out Double Brackets

There's a handy way to multiply double brackets — it's called the <u>FOIL</u> method and works like this:

<u>F</u>irst — multiply the first term in each bracket together

<u>O</u>utside — multiply the outside terms (i.e. the first term in the first bracket by the second term in the second bracket)

<u>I</u>nside — multiply the inside terms (i.e. the second term in the first bracket by the first term in the second bracket)

<u>L</u>ast — multiply the second term in each bracket together

When multiplying double brackets, you get <u>4 terms</u> — and 2 of them usually combine to leave <u>3 terms</u>.

EXAMPLES:

1. Expand and simplify $(x + 3)(x + 8)$

$$\qquad\qquad\qquad\ \ \text{F}\qquad\quad \text{O}\qquad\quad \text{I}\qquad\quad \text{L}$$
$$(x + 3)(x + 8) = (x \times x) + (x \times 8) + (3 \times x) + (3 \times 8)$$
$$= \quad x^2 \qquad + 8x \qquad + 3x \qquad + 24$$
$$= \quad x^2 + 11x + 24$$

The two x-terms <u>combine together</u>.

2. Expand and simplify $(n - 2)(2n + 7)$

$$\qquad\qquad\qquad\ \ \text{F}\qquad\quad \text{O}\qquad\quad \text{I}\qquad\qquad \text{L}$$
$$(n - 2)(2n + 7) = (n \times 2n) + (n \times 7) + (-2 \times 2n) + (-2 \times 7)$$
$$= \quad 2n^2 \qquad + 7n \qquad - 4n \qquad - 14$$
$$= \quad 2n^2 + 3n - 14$$

Write Out Squared Brackets as Double Brackets

Always write out <u>squared</u> brackets as <u>two brackets</u> (to avoid mistakes) — then multiply them out using the <u>FOIL</u> method above.

EXAMPLE: Expand and simplify $(3x + 2)^2$

$$(3x + 2)^2 = (3x + 2)(3x + 2)$$
$$= 9x^2 + 6x + 6x + 4$$
$$= 9x^2 + 12x + 4$$

Write out the expression as <u>two brackets</u>, then use the <u>FOIL</u> method.

DON'T make the mistake of thinking that $(3x + 2)^2 = 9x^2 + 4$ (this is <u>wrong wrong wrong</u>).

Go forth and multiply out brackets...

Don't rush when multiplying double brackets — you'll make mistakes and throw away easy marks. Have a go at these questions to see how it's done (expanding brackets, that is, not throwing away marks).

Q1 Expand and simplify: a) $(x + 6)(x - 5)$ [2 marks]   b) $(2y - 1)(y + 9)$ [2 marks]

Q2 Expand and simplify: a) $(x - 3)^2$ [2 marks]   b) $(4y + 5)^2$ [2 marks]

Factorising

Right, now you know how to expand brackets, it's time to put them back in. This is known as <u>factorising</u>.

Factorising — Putting Brackets In

This is the <u>exact reverse</u> of multiplying out brackets. You have to look for <u>common factors</u> — numbers or letters that go into <u>every term</u>. Here's the method to follow:

> 1) Take out the <u>biggest number</u> that goes into all the terms.
> 2) <u>For each letter in turn</u>, take out the <u>highest power</u> (e.g. x, x^2, etc.) that will go into EVERY term.
> 3) Open the bracket and fill in all the bits needed to <u>reproduce each term</u>.
> 4) <u>Check</u> your answer by <u>multiplying out</u> the bracket and making sure it matches the original expression.

EXAMPLES:

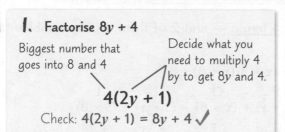

1. Factorise $8y + 4$

Biggest number that goes into 8 and 4

Decide what you need to multiply 4 by to get $8y$ and 4.

$$4(2y + 1)$$

Check: $4(2y + 1) = 8y + 4$ ✓

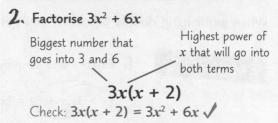

2. Factorise $3x^2 + 6x$

Biggest number that goes into 3 and 6

Highest power of x that will go into both terms

$$3x(x + 2)$$

Check: $3x(x + 2) = 3x^2 + 6x$ ✓

<u>REMEMBER</u>: The bits <u>taken out</u> and put at the front are the <u>common factors</u>. The bits <u>inside the bracket</u> are what's needed to get back to the <u>original terms</u> if you multiply the bracket out again.

D.O.T.S. — The Difference Of Two Squares

The 'difference of two squares' (D.O.T.S. for short) is where you have 'one thing squared' <u>take away</u> 'another thing squared'. There's a quick and easy way to factorise it — just use the rule below:

$$a^2 - b^2 = (a + b)(a - b)$$

EXAMPLE: Factorise:

a) $t^2 - 1$ Answer: $t^2 - 1 = (t + 1)(t - 1)$
Don't forget that 1 is a square number.

b) $s^2 - 64$ Answer: $s^2 - 64 = (s + 8)(s - 8)$
$64 = 8^2$, so in the formula above, b = 8.

c) $25m^2 - 1$ Answer: $25m^2 - 1 = (5m + 1)(5m - 1)$
Here you have to remember that it's 5m, not just m.

d) $9p^2 - 16q^2$ Answer: $9p^2 - 16q^2 = (3p + 4q)(3p - 4q)$
This time you had to spot that 9 and 16 are square numbers.

Well, one's green and one's yellow...

As factorising is the reverse process of expanding brackets, you <u>must check</u> your answer by multiplying out the brackets. Make sure you can spot differences of two squares as well — they can be a bit sneaky.

Q1   Factorise $12x + 30$ [1 mark]

Q2   Factorise $6y + 15y^2$ [2 marks]

Q3   Factorise $x^2 - 25$ [2 marks]

Q4   Factorise $36x^2 - 49y^2$ [2 marks]

Solving Equations

'Solving equations' basically means 'find the <u>value of x</u> (or whatever letter is used) that makes the equation <u>true</u>'. To do this, you usually have to <u>rearrange</u> the equation to get x <u>on its own</u>.

The 'Common Sense' Approach

The trick here is to realise that the <u>unknown quantity</u> 'x' is just a <u>number</u> and the '<u>equation</u>' is a <u>cryptic clue</u> to help you find it.

 Solve the equation $3x + 4 = 46$.

> This just means 'find the value of x'.

This is what you should say to yourself:

'Something + 4 = 46', hmmm, so that 'something' must be 42.

So that means $3x = 42$, which means '3 × something = 42'.

So it must be $42 ÷ 3 = 14$, so $x = 14$.

> If you were writing this down in an exam question, just write down the bits in blue.

In other words don't think of it as algebra, but as '<u>find the mystery number</u>'.

The 'Proper' Way

The 'proper' way to solve equations is to keep <u>rearranging</u> them until you end up with '<u>x = </u>' on one side. There are a few <u>important points</u> to remember when rearranging.

Golden Rules

1) Always do the <u>SAME thing</u> to <u>both sides of the equation</u>.
2) To get rid of something, do the <u>opposite</u>.
   The opposite of + is − and the opposite of − is +.
   The opposite of × is ÷ and the opposite of ÷ is ×.
3) Keep going until you have a letter <u>on its own</u>.

EXAMPLES:

1. Solve $x + 7 = 11$.

> The opposite of +7 is −7

$$x + 7 = 11$$
$$(-7) \quad x + 7 - 7 = 11 - 7$$
$$x = 4$$

> This means 'take away 7 from both sides'.

2. Solve $x - 3 = 7$.

> The opposite of −3 is +3

$$x - 3 = 7$$
$$(+3) \quad x - 3 + 3 = 7 + 3$$
$$x = 10$$

3. Solve $5x = 15$.

> 5x means 5 × x, so do the opposite — divide both sides by 5

$$5x = 15$$
$$(÷5) \quad 5x ÷ 5 = 15 ÷ 5$$
$$x = 3$$

4. Solve $\frac{x}{3} = 2$.

> $\frac{x}{3}$ means x ÷ 3, so do the opposite — multiply both sides by 3

$$\frac{x}{3} = 2$$
$$(×3) \quad \frac{x}{3} × 3 = 2 × 3$$
$$x = 6$$

Handy hint — x often hides behind the sofa...

It's a good idea to write down what you're doing at every stage — put it in brackets next to the equation (like in the examples above). Try it out on this Exam Practice Question.

Q1   Solve these equations: a) $x + 2 = 8$ [1 mark]   b) $x - 6 = 8$ [1 mark]
                         c) $4x = 12$ [1 mark]   d) $\frac{x}{5} = 3$ [1 mark]

Solving Equations

You're not done with solving equations yet — not by a long shot. This is where it gets <u>really fun</u>*.

Two-Step Equations

If you come across an equation like $4x + 3 = 19$ (where there's an <u>x-term</u> and a <u>number</u> on the <u>same side</u>), use the methods from the previous page to solve it — just do it in <u>two steps</u>:

1) <u>Add or subtract</u> the number first.   2) <u>Multiply or divide</u> to get 'x = '.

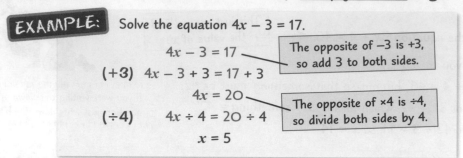

EXAMPLE: Solve the equation $4x - 3 = 17$.

$$4x - 3 = 17$$
The opposite of −3 is +3, so add 3 to both sides.

$(+3)$ $4x - 3 + 3 = 17 + 3$

$$4x = 20$$
The opposite of ×4 is ÷4, so divide both sides by 4.

$(\div 4)$ $4x \div 4 = 20 \div 4$

$$x = 5$$

Equations with an 'x' on Both Sides

For equations like $2x + 3 = x + 7$ (where there's an x-term on <u>each side</u>), you have to:

1) Get all the x's on one side and all the <u>numbers</u> on the other.

2) <u>Multiply or divide</u> to get 'x = '.

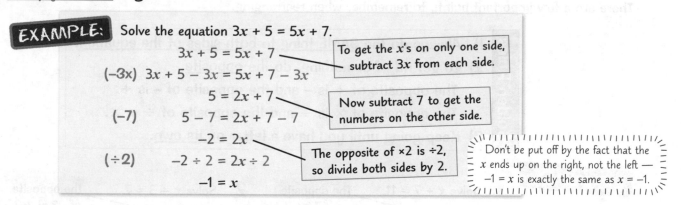

EXAMPLE: Solve the equation $3x + 5 = 5x + 7$.

$$3x + 5 = 5x + 7$$
To get the x's on only one side, subtract 3x from each side.

$(-3x)$ $3x + 5 - 3x = 5x + 7 - 3x$

$$5 = 2x + 7$$
Now subtract 7 to get the numbers on the other side.

(-7) $5 - 7 = 2x + 7 - 7$

$$-2 = 2x$$
The opposite of ×2 is ÷2, so divide both sides by 2.

$(\div 2)$ $-2 \div 2 = 2x \div 2$

$$-1 = x$$

Don't be put off by the fact that the x ends up on the right, not the left — $-1 = x$ is exactly the same as $x = -1$.

Equations with Brackets

If the equation has <u>brackets</u> in, you have to <u>multiply out</u> the brackets (see p.26) before solving it as above.

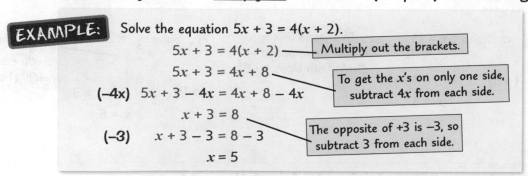

EXAMPLE: Solve the equation $5x + 3 = 4(x + 2)$.

$$5x + 3 = 4(x + 2)$$
Multiply out the brackets.

$$5x + 3 = 4x + 8$$
To get the x's on only one side, subtract 4x from each side.

$(-4x)$ $5x + 3 - 4x = 4x + 8 - 4x$

$$x + 3 = 8$$
The opposite of +3 is −3, so subtract 3 from each side.

(-3) $x + 3 - 3 = 8 - 3$

$$x = 5$$

Solving mysteries would be more exciting...

A good thing about solving equations is that you can always check your answer — just put the value of x you've found back into the original equation, and check that it works. Give it a go on these questions.

Q1   Solve $6x - 5 = 3x + 10$ [2 marks] (3)   Q2   Solve $4(y - 2) = 2y + 6$ [3 marks] (4)

*Fun not guaranteed. Terms and conditions apply.

Expressions, Formulas and Functions

Before we get started, there are a few <u>definitions</u> you need to know:

> 1) **EXPRESSION** — a <u>collection</u> of <u>terms</u> (see p.25). Expressions <u>DON'T</u> have an = sign in them.
> 2) **EQUATION** — an expression with an = sign in it (so you can solve it)
> 3) **FORMULA** — a <u>rule</u> that helps you work something out (it will also have an = sign in it).
> 4) **FUNCTION** — an expression that takes an <u>input</u> value, <u>processes</u> it and produces an <u>output</u> value.

Putting Numbers into Formulas

You might be given a <u>formula</u> and asked to work out its <u>value</u> when you put in <u>certain numbers</u>.
All you have to do here is follow this <u>method</u>.

> 1) Write out the <u>formula</u>.
> 2) Write it <u>again</u>, directly underneath, but <u>substituting numbers for letters</u> on the <u>RHS</u> (right-hand side).
> 3) Work it out <u>in stages</u>. Use <u>BODMAS</u> (see p.2) to work things out in the <u>right order</u>. <u>Write down</u> values for each bit as you go along.
> 4) <u>DO NOT</u> attempt to do it <u>all in one go</u> on your calculator — you're more likely to make <u>mistakes</u>.

EXAMPLE: The formula for converting from Celsius (C) to Fahrenheit (F) is $F = \frac{9}{5}C + 32$.
Use this formula to convert $-10\ °C$ into Fahrenheit.

$F = \frac{9}{5}C + 32$ ——— 1) Write out the <u>formula</u>.

$F = \frac{9}{5} \times -10 + 32$ ——— 2) Write it <u>again</u>, substituting numbers for letters on the <u>RHS</u>.

$F = -18 + 32$ ——— 3) Use <u>BODMAS</u> to work things out in the <u>right order</u> — do the <u>multiplication</u> first, then do the <u>addition</u>.

$F = 14$ so $-10\ °C = 14\ °F$

> Be careful when substituting negative numbers into a formula — just do it step-by-step.

Functions Produce Outputs from Inputs

> 1) A <u>function</u> takes an <u>input</u>, <u>processes</u> it (e.g. multiplies it by 5 and adds 2) and <u>outputs</u> a value.
> 2) If you have to use a <u>function machine</u>, just put in the number, follow the steps and see what comes out.
> 3) If you're given the <u>output</u> and have to find the <u>input</u>, use the function machine <u>in reverse</u>.

EXAMPLE: The function machine below represents the function 'multiply by 5 and add 2'.

$x \longrightarrow$ [× 5] $\longrightarrow$ [+ 2] $\longrightarrow y$

> If this was an equation, it'd be written as $y = 5x + 2$.

a) Find the value of y when $x = 5$.
Just put 5 into the machine: $5 \xrightarrow{\times 5} 25 \xrightarrow{+2} 27$. So $y = 27$.

b) Find the value of x when $y = 42$.
This time, put $y = 42$ into the machine and <u>work backwards</u>:
$42 \xrightarrow{-2} 40 \xrightarrow{\div 5} 8$. So $x = 8$.

> Don't forget to reverse each step as well — so +2 becomes −2 and ×5 becomes ÷5.

Grumpiness = number of annoying people ÷ hours of sleep...

If you have more than one number to put into a formula, make sure you put them in the right places.

Q1 $v = u + at$. Find the value of v when $u = 5$, $a = 4$ and $t = 6$.   [2 marks]

Q2   Using the function machine above, find the value of x when $y = 57$.   [2 marks]

Formulas and Equations from Words

Making <u>expressions</u> or <u>formulas</u> from <u>words</u> can be a bit confusing as you're given a lot of <u>information</u> in one go. You just have to go through it slowly and carefully and <u>extract the maths</u> from it.

Make Expressions or Formulas from Given Information

Here are some of <u>examples</u> of how to use the information to write expressions and formulas.

 Tiana is x years old. Leah is 5 years younger than Tiana. Martin is 4 times as old as Tiana. Find a simplified expression for the sum of their ages in terms of x.

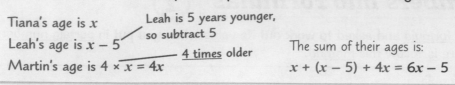

Tiana's age is x
Leah is 5 years younger, so subtract 5
Leah's age is $x - 5$
Martin's age is $4 \times x = 4x$ 4 times older

The sum of their ages is:
$x + (x - 5) + 4x = 6x - 5$

If you'd been <u>told</u> the sum of their ages, you'd have to set your expression equal to the sum and solve it to find x.

 In rugby union, tries score 5 points and conversions score 2 points. A team scores a total of P points, made up of t tries and c conversions. Write a formula for P in terms of t and c.

Tries score 5 points —— t tries will score $5 \times t = 5t$ points
Conversions score 2 points —— c conversions will score $2 \times c = 2c$ points
So total points scored are $P = 5t + 2c$

Because you're asked for a formula, you must include the 'P = ' bit to get full marks (i.e. don't just put $5t + 2c$).

Use Your Expression to Solve Equations

Sometimes, you might be asked to <u>use</u> an expression to <u>solve an equation</u>.

 A zoo has x zebras and four times as many lemurs. The difference between the number of zebras and the number of lemurs is 45. How many zebras does the zoo have?

The zoo has x zebras and $4 \times x = 4x$ lemurs.
The difference is $4x - x = 3x$, so $3x = 45$, which means $x = 15$.
So the zoo has **15 zebras**.

Once you've formed the equation, you need to solve it to find the value of x.

 Will, Naveed and Camille give some books to charity. Naveed gives 6 more books than Will, and Camille gives 7 more books than Naveed. Between them, they give away 46 books. How many books did they give each?

Let the number of books Will gives be x.
Then Naveed gives $x + 6$ books
and Camille gives $(x + 6) + 7 = x + 13$ books
So in total they give $x + x + 6 + x + 13 = 3x + 19$ books

So $3x + 19 = 46$ —— You're told this in the question.
$3x = 27$
$x = 9$

So Will gives **9 books**,
Naveed gives $9 + 6 = $ **15 books** and
Camille gives $15 + 7 = $ **22 books**.

I have the formula for the perfect cup of tea...

Exam questions might not tell you to write an equation or formula, sometimes you have to come up with one for yourself to be able to answer the question. Try writing some for these Exam Practice Questions.

Q1   Ali, Ben and Joe sell 73 raffle tickets between them. Ben sells twice as many tickets as Ali, and Joe sells 8 more tickets than Ben. How many tickets does each person sell?   [3 marks]

Q2   Three positive whole numbers have a sum of 48. The second number is five times the first, and the third number is double the second number. What are the three numbers?   [3 marks]

Formulas and Equations from Diagrams

Formulas and equations can even sneak into <u>area</u> and <u>perimeter</u> questions — have a look at pages 78-79 if you need to brush up on those topics.

Use Shape Properties to Find Formulas and Equations

In some questions, you'll need to use what you know about <u>shapes</u> (e.g. <u>side lengths</u> or <u>areas</u>) to come up with a formula or an equation to solve.

 **EXAMPLE:**

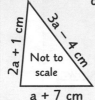

a) Write a formula for P, the perimeter of the triangle below, in terms of a.

Form an <u>expression</u> for the <u>perimeter</u>:
$P = (a + 7) + (2a + 1) + (3a − 4)$
$P = 6a + 4$ cm

b) If the triangle has a perimeter of 58 cm, find the value of a.

P = 58, so set your formula equal to <u>58</u> and <u>solve</u> to find a:
$6a + 4 = 58$
$6a = 54$
$a = 9$

Compare Dimensions of Two Shapes to Find Equations

You might get a question that involves <u>two shapes</u> with related <u>areas</u> or <u>perimeters</u> — you'll have to use this fact to find <u>side lengths</u> or <u>missing values</u>.

 **EXAMPLE:**

The perimeter of the rectangle is the same as the perimeter of the square. Find the value of x.

Perimeter of square = $2x + 2x + 2x + 2x = 8x$ cm
Perimeter of rectangle = $(2x + 5) + (x − 2) + (2x + 5) + (x − 2)$
$= 6x + 6$ cm

Set the perimeter of the rectangle equal to the perimeter of the square and solve:

$8x = 6x + 6$
$2x = 6$
$x = 3$

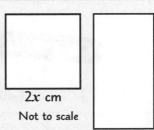

2x cm

Not to scale

x − 2 cm

EXAMPLE:

The area of the square is the same as the area of the triangle. Find the length of the base of the triangle.

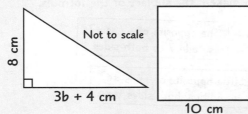

Not to scale

8 cm

3b + 4 cm

10 cm

Area of triangle: $\frac{1}{2} × (3b + 4) × 8 = 12b + 16$ cm^2
Area of square: $10^2 = 100$ cm^2

Set the areas equal to each other and solve:
$12b + 16 = 100$
$12b = 84$
$b = 7$
So base length = $(3 × 7) + 4 = 25$ cm

Perimeter? Area? I thought this was an algebra section...

Don't be put off by the shapey words — once you've turned the information into an equation, it's just normal algebra (though I'm not sure if that makes it better or worse...). Anyway, try this question.

Q1   A regular pentagon has sides of length x cm. A square with sides of length $x + 4$ cm has the same perimeter as the pentagon. Find the value of x.   [3 marks]

Rearranging Formulas

The <u>subject</u> of a formula is the letter <u>on its own</u> before the = (so x is the subject of x = 2y + 3z).

Changing the Subject of a Formula

<u>Rearranging formulas</u> means making a different letter the <u>subject</u>, e.g. getting 'y = ' from 'x = 3y + 2'.
Fortunately, you can use the <u>same methods</u> that you used for <u>solving equations</u> (see p29-30)
— here's a quick reminder:

Golden Rules

1) Always do the <u>SAME</u> thing to <u>both sides of the formula</u>.
2) To get rid of something, do the <u>opposite</u>.
   The opposite of + is − and the opposite of − is +.
   The opposite of × is ÷ and the opposite of ÷ is ×.
3) Keep going until you have the letter you want <u>on its own</u>.

EXAMPLE: Rearrange a = 3b + 4 to make b the subject of the formula.

$$a = 3b + 4$$

> The opposite of +4 is −4, so take away 4 from both sides.

$$(-4) \quad a - 4 = 3b + 4 - 4$$

$$a - 4 = 3b$$

> The opposite of ×3 is ÷3, so divide both sides by 3.

$$(\div 3) \quad (a - 4) \div 3 = 3b \div 3$$

> Careful here — you divide the <u>whole side</u> by 3, not just one term.

$$\frac{a - 4}{3} = b \quad \text{OR} \quad b = \frac{a - 4}{3}$$

EXAMPLE: Rearrange p = 5(q + 2) to make q the subject of the formula.

$$p = 5q + 10$$

> Multiply out the brackets.

$$(-10) \quad p - 10 = 5q + 10 - 10$$

> The opposite of +10 is −10, so take away 10 from both sides.

$$p - 10 = 5q$$

$$(\div 5) \quad (p - 10) \div 5 = 5q \div 5$$

> The opposite of ×5 is ÷5, so divide both sides by 5.

$$\frac{p - 10}{5} = q \quad \text{OR} \quad q = \frac{p - 10}{5}$$

EXAMPLE: Rearrange $m = \frac{n}{4} - 7$ to make n the subject of the formula.

$$m = \frac{n}{4} - 7$$

> The opposite of −7 is +7, so add 7 to both sides.

$$(+7) \quad m + 7 = \frac{n}{4} - 7 + 7$$

$$m + 7 = \frac{n}{4}$$

> The opposite of ÷4 is ×4, so multiply both sides by 4.

$$(\times 4) \quad (m + 7) \times 4 = \frac{n}{4} \times 4$$

$$4(m + 7) = n \quad \text{OR} \quad n = 4m + 28$$

If I could rearrange my subjects I'd have Maths all day every day...

This page is really just like solving equations — so if you learn the method for one, you know
the method for the other. What a bonus. It's like buy-one-get-one-free but more mathsy.

Q1   Rearrange $u = \frac{v}{3} - 2$ to make v the subject of the formula.   [2 marks]

Q2   Rearrange $c = 6d - 12$ to make d the subject of the formula.   [2 marks]

Sequences

Sequences are <u>lists</u> of numbers or shapes that follow a <u>rule</u>. You need to be able to spot what the rule is.

Finding the Rule for Number Sequences

The trick to <u>finding the rule</u> for number sequences is to <u>write down</u> what you have to do to get from one number to the next in the <u>gaps</u> between the numbers. There are <u>2 main types</u> to look out for:

1) <u>Add</u> or <u>subtract</u> the <u>same number</u>   These are known as <u>arithmetic</u> sequences.

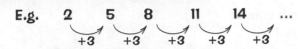

E.g. 2 5 8 11 14 ...   30 24 18 12 ...
      +3 +3 +3 +3 +3   −6 −6 −6 −6

The RULE: 'Add 3 to the <u>previous term</u>'   'Subtract 6 from the <u>previous term</u>'

2) <u>Multiply</u> or <u>divide</u> by the <u>same</u> number <u>each time</u>   These are known as <u>geometric</u> sequences.

 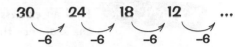

E.g. 2 6 18 54 ...   40 000 4000 400 40 ...
      ×3 ×3 ×3 ×3   ÷10 ÷10 ÷10 ÷10

The RULE: 'Multiply the <u>previous term</u> by 3'   'Divide the <u>previous term</u> by 10'

Sometimes you might get sequences that follow a <u>different</u> rule — e.g. you might have to add or subtract a <u>changing number</u> each time, or add together the <u>two previous terms</u> (see the examples below).

EXAMPLE: Find the next two terms in each of the following sequences.

a) 1, 3, 6, 10, 15, ...

'<u>The number you add on increases by one each time</u>' (i.e. +2, +3, +4, ...) so the next two terms are:

15 + 6 = 21   This is the sequence of
21 + 7 = 28   triangular numbers.

b) 1, 1, 2, 3, 5, ...

The rule is '<u>add together the two previous terms</u>', so the next two terms are:

3 + 5 = 8   This is known as the
5 + 8 = 13   Fibonacci sequence.

Finding the Rule for Shape Sequences

If you have a sequence of <u>shape</u> patterns, you need to be able to <u>continue</u> the sequence. You might also have to find the <u>rule</u> for the sequence to work out <u>how many</u> shapes there'll be in a later pattern.

EXAMPLE: On the right, there are some patterns made of circles.
a) Draw the next pattern in the sequence.
b) Work out how many circles there will be in the 10th pattern.

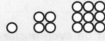

a) Just continue the sequence — the circles make a <u>square pattern</u>. ⟶

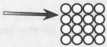

b) Find the rule for the number of circles: there's $1^2 = 1$ **circle** in the first pattern, $2^2 = 4$ **circles** in the second pattern, $3^2 = 9$ **circles** in the third pattern etc. The rule is '**square the number of the pattern**'. So in the 10th pattern, there'll be $10^2 = 100$ **circles**.

Knitting patterns follow the rule knit one, purl one...

Remember, you always need to work out what to do to get from one term to the next — that's the rule.

Q1   A sequence starts 3, 6, 12, ... There are two possible rules for this sequence. Write down both possible rules and find the next two terms of the sequence in each case.   **[2 marks]** **(3)**

Sequences

If the examiners are feeling mean, they might ask you to "find an <u>expression</u> for the <u>nth term</u> of a sequence" — this is a rule with n in, like 5n − 3. It gives <u>every term in a sequence</u> when you put in different values for n.

Finding the nth Term of a Sequence

This method works for sequences with a <u>common difference</u> — where you <u>add</u> or <u>subtract</u> the <u>same number</u> each time.

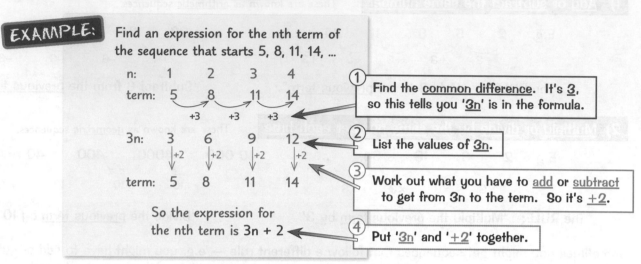

EXAMPLE:

Find an expression for the nth term of the sequence that starts 5, 8, 11, 14, ...

n:	1	2	3	4
term:	5	8	11	14

+3 +3 +3

3n:	3	6	9	12

+2 +2 +2 +2

term:	5	8	11	14

So the expression for the nth term is 3n + 2

① Find the <u>common difference</u>. It's <u>3</u>, so this tells you '<u>3n</u>' is in the formula.

② List the values of <u>3n</u>.

③ Work out what you have to <u>add</u> or <u>subtract</u> to get from 3n to the term. So it's <u>+2</u>.

④ Put '<u>3n</u>' and '<u>+2</u>' together.

<u>Check</u> your formula by putting the first few values of n back in:
n = 1 gives 3n + 2 = 3 + 2 = 5 ✓
n = 2 gives 3n + 2 = 6 + 2 = 8 ✓

Deciding if a Term is in a Sequence

You might be given the nth term and asked if a <u>certain value</u> is in the sequence. The trick here is to <u>set the expression equal to that value</u> and solve to find n. If n is a <u>whole number</u>, the value is <u>in</u> the sequence.

EXAMPLE:

A sequence is given by the rule 6n − 2.

a) Find the 6th term in the sequence.

Just put n = 6 into the expression:
(6 × 6) − 2 = 36 − 2
= 34

b) Is 45 a term in this sequence?

Set it equal to 45...   6n − 2 = 45
6n = 47   ...and solve for n.
n = 47 ÷ 6 = 7.8333...

n is not a whole number, so 45 is <u>not</u> in the sequence 6n − 2.

Have a look at p.29-30 for more on solving equations.

It might be even <u>easier</u> to decide if a number is in a sequence or not — for example, if the sequence was all <u>odd numbers</u>, there's <u>no way</u> that an <u>even number</u> could be in the sequence. You just have to use your common sense — e.g. if all the terms in the sequence ended in <u>3</u> or <u>8</u>, 44 would <u>not</u> be in the sequence.

If I've told you n times, I've told you n + 1 times — learn this page...

This is a bit trickier than the other stuff on sequences, but at least there's a way to check your answer. The only way to get good at finding the rule is practice — so have a go at this Exam Practice Question.

Q1   A sequence starts 2, 9, 16, 23, ...
a) Find an expression for the nth term of the sequence.   [2 marks]
b) Use your expression to find the 8th term in the sequence.   [1 mark]
c) Is 63 a term in the sequence? Explain your answer.   [2 marks]

Inequalities

Inequalities are a bit tricky, but once you've learned the tricks involved, most of the algebra for them is identical to ordinary equations (have a look back at pages 29-30 if you need a reminder).

The Inequality Symbols

I > All of you.

> means 'Greater than'   ≥ means 'Greater than or equal to'
< means 'Less than'   ≤ means 'Less than or equal to'

REMEMBER — the one at the BIG end is BIGGEST so x > 4 and 4 < x both say: 'x is greater than 4'.

EXAMPLE: x is an integer such that $-4 < x \leq 3$. Write down all possible values of x.

Work out what each bit of the inequality is telling you:

$-4 < x$ means 'x is greater than -4',

and $x \leq 3$ means 'x is less than or equal to 3'.

Now just write down all the values that x can take:

$$-3, -2, -1, 0, 1, 2, 3$$

Remember, integers are just whole numbers (+ve and −ve, including 0).

−4 isn't included because of the < but 3 is included because of the ≤.

You Can Show Inequalities on Number Lines

Drawing inequalities on a number line is dead easy — all you have to remember is that you use an open circle (○) for > or < and a coloured-in circle (●) for ≥ or ≤.

EXAMPLE: Show the inequality $-4 < x \leq 3$ on a number line.

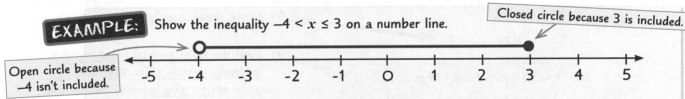

Closed circle because 3 is included.

Open circle because −4 isn't included.

Algebra with Inequalities

Solve inequalities like regular equations but WITH ONE BIG EXCEPTION:

Whenever you MULTIPLY OR DIVIDE by a NEGATIVE NUMBER, you must FLIP THE INEQUALITY SIGN.

EXAMPLES:

1. Solve $3x - 2 \leq 13$.

Just solve it like an equation — but leave the inequality sign in your answer:

(+2) $3x - 2 + 2 \leq 13 + 2$
$3x \leq 15$
(÷3) $3x \div 3 \leq 15 \div 3$
$x \leq 5$

2. Solve $2x + 7 > x + 11$.

Again, solve it like an equation:

(−7) $2x + 7 - 7 > x + 11 - 7$
$2x > x + 4$
(−x) $2x - x > x + 4 - x$
$x > 4$

3. Solve $9 - 2x > 15$.

Watch out for the sign change:

(−9) $9 - 2x - 9 > 15 - 9$
$-2x > 6$
(÷−2) $-2x \div -2 < 6 \div -2$
$x < -3$

The > has turned into a <, because we divided by a negative number.

I saw you flip the inequality sign — how rude...

To check you've got the inequality sign right, pop in a value for x and check the inequality's true.

Q1 n is an integer such that $-1 \leq n < 5$. Write down all the possible values of n. [2 marks]

Q2   Solve the following inequalities: a) $4x + 3 < 27$ [2 marks]   b) $4x \geq 18 - 2x$ [2 marks]

Quadratic Equations

A __quadratic__ equation is one where the highest power is x^2.
The standard format for a quadratic equation is $\underline{x^2 + bx + c = 0}$.

You can Factorise Quadratic Equations (5)

1) You can __solve__ quadratic equations by __factorising__.

2) '__Factorising a quadratic__' means '__putting it into 2 brackets__'.

> **Factorising Quadratics**
>
> 1) __ALWAYS__ rearrange into the __STANDARD FORMAT__: $x^2 + bx + c = 0$.
>
> 2) Write down the __TWO BRACKETS__ with the x's in: $(x \quad)(x \quad) = 0$.
>
> 3) Then __find 2 numbers__ that __MULTIPLY to give 'c'__ (the number term) but also __ADD/SUBTRACT to give 'b'__ (the number in front of the x term).
>
> 4) Fill in the +/– signs and make sure they work out properly.
>
> 5) As an __ESSENTIAL CHECK__, __EXPAND__ the brackets to make sure they give the original equation.

Ignore any minus signs at this stage.

3) As well as factorising a quadratic, you might be asked to __solve__ the equation. This just means finding the values of x that make each bracket __0__ (see example below).

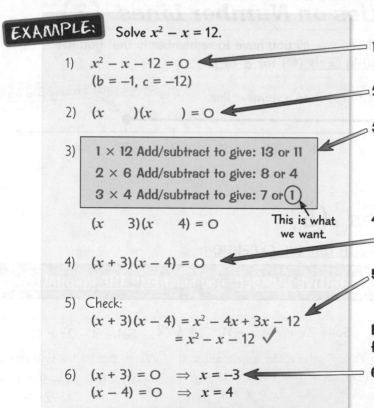

EXAMPLE: Solve $x^2 - x = 12$.

1) $x^2 - x - 12 = 0$
   $(b = -1, c = -12)$

2) $(x \quad)(x \quad) = 0$

3) 1×12 Add/subtract to give: 13 or 11
   2×6 Add/subtract to give: 8 or 4
   3×4 Add/subtract to give: 7 or ①

   This is what we want.

   $(x \quad 3)(x \quad 4) = 0$

4) $(x + 3)(x - 4) = 0$

5) Check:
   $(x + 3)(x - 4) = x^2 - 4x + 3x - 12$
   $= x^2 - x - 12$ ✓

6) $(x + 3) = 0 \Rightarrow x = -3$
   $(x - 4) = 0 \Rightarrow x = 4$

1) __Rearrange__ into the standard format.

2) Write down __two brackets__ with x's in.

3) Find the right __pair of numbers__ that __multiply to give c__ (= 12), and __add or subtract to give b__ (= 1) (remember, we're ignoring the +/– signs for now).

4) __Now fill in the +/– signs__ so that 3 and 4 add/subtract to give –1 (= b).

5) __ESSENTIAL check__ — __EXPAND the brackets__ to make sure they give the original expression.

   But we're not finished yet — we've only factorised it, we still need to...

6) __SOLVE THE EQUATION__ by setting each bracket __equal to 0__.

To help you work out which __signs__ you need, __look at c__.

- If c is __positive__, the signs will be __the same__ — both positive or both negative.
- If c is __negative__ the signs will be __different__ — one positive and one negative.

Bring me a biscuit or I'll factorise your quadratic...

Don't worry if this stuff looks horrible and you find it difficult at first — it's a really tricky topic.
Just keep going over the example until it starts to make sense. Then try these Exam Practice Questions.

Q1   Factorise $x^2 + 2x - 15$ [2 marks] (5)   Q2   Solve $x^2 - 9x + 20 = 0$ [3 marks] (5)

Simultaneous Equations

Simultaneous equations might sound a bit scary, but they're just a pair of equations that you have to solve at the same time. You have to find values of x and y that work in both equations.

Six Steps for Simultaneous Equations

EXAMPLE: Solve the simultaneous equations $2x + 4y = 6$
$4x + 3y = -3$

Both your equations should be in the form ax + by = c, where a, b and c are numbers.

1. **Label** your equations ① and ②.

   $2x + 4y = 6$ — ①
   $4x + 3y = -3$ — ②

2. **Match up the numbers in front** of either the x's or y's in both equations. You may need to multiply one or both equations by a suitable number. Relabel the equations ③ and ④ if you need to change them.

   ① × 2: $4x + 8y = 12$ — ③
   $4x + 3y = -3$ — ②

   You don't need to change equation 2 for this example.

3. **Add or subtract the two equations** to eliminate the terms with the same number in front.

   ③ − ②: $\begin{array}{r} 4x + 8y = 12 \\ -\ 4x + 3y = -3 \\ \hline 0x + 5y = 15 \end{array}$

   If the numbers have the same sign (both +ve or both −ve) then subtract. If the numbers have opposite signs (one +ve and one −ve) then add.

4. **Solve** the resulting equation.

   $5y = 15 \Rightarrow y = 3$

5. **Substitute** the value you've found back into equation ① and **solve it**.

   Sub $y = 3$ into ①: $2x + (4 \times 3) = 6 \Rightarrow 2x + 12 = 6 \Rightarrow 2x = -6 \Rightarrow x = -3$

6. **Substitute** both these values into equation ② to make sure it works. If it doesn't then you've done something wrong and you'll have to do it all again.

   Sub x and y into ②: $(4 \times -3) + (3 \times 3) = -12 + 9 = -3$, which is right, so it's worked.
   So the solutions are: $x = -3$, $y = 3$

I can drink tea and read a book simultaneously...

Simultaneous equations can be a really tough topic — look over the example a few times until you get it. Then, when you've learnt the 6 steps on this page you'll be ready to tackle some Exam Practice Questions.

Q1 Solve the simultaneous equations $\quad x + y = 3$
$\quad\quad\quad\quad\quad\quad\quad\quad\quad\quad\quad\quad\quad 4x + 3y = 10$ [3 marks]

Q2 Solve the simultaneous equations $\quad 2x + 4y = 2$
$\quad\quad\quad\quad\quad\quad\quad\quad\quad\quad\quad\quad\quad 5x - 3y = 18$ [3 marks]

Proof

I'm not going to lie — <u>proof questions</u> can look a bit terrifying. But there are a couple of tricks you can use that makes them a bit less scary.

Prove Statements are True or False

1) The most straightforward proofs are ones where you're given a <u>statement</u> and asked if it's <u>true</u> or <u>false</u>.

2) To show that it's <u>false</u>, all you have to do is find <u>one example</u> that doesn't <u>work</u>.

3) Showing that something is <u>true</u> is a bit trickier — you might have to do a bit of <u>rearranging</u> to show that two things are <u>equal</u>, or show that one thing is a <u>multiple</u> of a certain number.

 EXAMPLE: Find an example to show that the statement below is not correct.
"The difference between two prime numbers is always even."

2 and 5 are both prime, so try them:

$5 - 2 = 3$, which is odd — so the statement is not correct.

It was easy to find an example for this one — but sometimes you might have to try a few different numbers to find a pair that doesn't work.

 **EXAMPLE:** Prove that $(n + 3)^2 - (n - 2)^2 \equiv 5(2n + 1)$.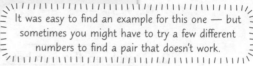
Take one side of the equation and play about with it until you get the other side:

$$\text{LHS: } (n + 3)^2 - (n - 2)^2 \equiv n^2 + 6n + 9 - (n^2 - 4n + 4)$$
$$\equiv n^2 + 6n + 9 - n^2 + 4n - 4$$
$$\equiv 10n + 5$$
$$\equiv 5(2n + 1) = \text{RHS} \checkmark$$

See p.28 for a reminder on factorising.

> $\equiv$ is the <u>identity symbol</u>, and means that two things are <u>identically equal</u> to each other. So $a + b \equiv b + a$ is true for <u>all values</u> of a and b (unlike an equation, which is only true for certain values).

Show that One Thing is a Multiple of Another

1) To show that one thing is a <u>multiple</u> of a particular number (let's say <u>5</u>), you need to <u>rearrange</u> the thing you're given to get it into the form <u>5 × a whole number</u>, which means it's a multiple of 5.

2) If it <u>can't</u> be written as 5 × a whole number, then it's <u>not</u> a multiple of 5.

 EXAMPLE: $a = 3(b + 9) + 5(b - 2) + 3$.
Show that a is a multiple of 4 for any whole number value of b.

$a = 3(b + 9) + 5(b - 2) + 3$
$= 3b + 27 + 5b - 10 + 3$ —— Expand the brackets...
$= 8b + 20$ —————— ... simplify...
$= 4(2b + 5)$ ————— ... and factorise.

$2b + 5$ is a whole number because b is a whole number.

a can be written as 4 × something (where the something is $2b + 5$) so it is a multiple of 4.

3) It's always a good idea to keep in mind what you're <u>aiming for</u> — here, you're trying to write the expression for a as '<u>4 × a whole number</u>', so you'll need to take out a <u>factor of 4</u> at some point.

Prove that maths isn't fun...

The fancy name for finding an example that doesn't work is 'disproof by counter-example'.

Q1 For each of the following statements, find an example to prove that they are false.
a) All square numbers end in 1, 4, 6 or 9. [1 mark]
b) The product of two prime numbers is always odd. [1 mark]

Revision Questions for Section Two

There was a lot of <u>nasty algebra</u> in that section — let's see how much you remember.

- Try these questions and <u>tick off each one</u> when you <u>get it right</u>.
- When you've done <u>all the questions</u> for a topic and are <u>completely happy</u> with it, tick off the topic.

Algebra (p25-28) ☑

1) Simplify: a) $e + e + e$ b) $6f + 7f - f$
2) Simplify: a) $2x + 3y + 5x - 4y$ b) $11a + 2 - 8a + 7$
3) Simplify: a) $m \times m \times m$ b) $p \times q \times 7$ c) $2x \times 9y$
4) Expand: a) $6(x + 3)$ b) $-3(3x - 4)$ c) $x(5 - x)$
5) Expand and simplify $4(3 + 5x) - 2(7x + 6)$
6) Expand and simplify: a) $(x + 2)(2x - 5)$ b) $(5y + 2)^2$
7) What is factorising?
8) Factorise: a) $8x + 24$ b) $18x^2 + 27x$ c) $36x^2 - 81y^2$

Solving Equations (p29-30) ☑

9) Solve: a) $x + 9 = 16$ b) $x - 4 = 12$ c) $6x = 18$
10) Solve: a) $4x + 3 = 19$ b) $3x + 6 = x + 10$ c) $3(x + 2) = 5x$

Expressions, Functions and Formulas (p31-34) ☑

11) $Q = 5r + 6s$. Work out the value of Q when $r = -2$ and $s = 3$.
12) A function takes a number, doubles it and subtracts 8.
    What is the result when 11 is put in the machine?
13) Tony and Robbie have the same number of marbles. Nadia has 26 marbles.
    Between them, they have 100 marbles. How many marbles does Tony have?
14) A rectangle measures $2x$ cm by $7x$ cm. An equilateral triangle has the same perimeter
    as the rectangle. Find the length of one side of the triangle in terms of x.
15) Rearrange the formula $W = 4v + 5$ to make v the subject.

Sequences (p35-36) ☑

16) For each of the following sequences, find the next term and write down the rule you used.
    a) 3, 10, 17, 24, ...   b) 1, 4, 16, 64, ...   c) 2, 5, 7, 12, ...
17) Find an expression for the nth term of the sequence that starts 4, 10, 16, 22, ...
18) Is 34 a term in the sequence given by the expression $7n - 1$?

Inequalities and Quadratic Equations (p37-38) ☑

19) Write the following inequalities out in words: a) $x > -7$ b) $x \leq 6$
20) $0 < k \leq 7$. Find all the possible integer values of k.
21) Solve the following inequalities: a) $x + 4 < 14$ b) $3x + 5 \leq 26$.
22) Factorise the following quadratic expressions: a) $x^2 + 10x + 16$ b) $x^2 - 6x - 7$
23) Solve the quadratic equation $x^2 + 3x - 18 = 0$.

Simultaneous Equations and Proof (p39-40) ☑

24) Solve the following pair of simultaneous equations: $4x + 5y = 33$ and $-x + 3y = 13$
25) Find an example to show that the statement
    "if a number ends in a 9, it must divide by 3" is not true.
26) Show that x is never a multiple of 5 if $x = 3(y + 2) + 2(y + 6)$ for any whole number y.

Coordinates and Midpoints

What could be more fun than points in one quadrant? Points in <u>four quadrants</u>, that's what...

The Four Quadrants

A graph has <u>four different quadrants</u> (regions).

The top-right region is the easiest because <u>**ALL THE COORDINATES IN IT ARE POSITIVE**</u>.

You have to be careful in the <u>other regions</u> though, because the x- and y- coordinates could be <u>negative</u>, and that makes life much more difficult.

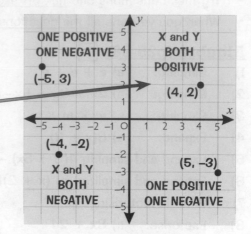

THREE IMPORTANT POINTS ABOUT COORDINATES:

1) The coordinates are always in <u>**ALPHABETICAL ORDER**</u>, x then y. $(\,x\,,\,y\,)$

2) x is always the flat axis going <u>ACROSS</u> the page.
   In other words '<u>x is a...cross</u>'   Get it — x is a 'x'.   (Hilarious isn't it)

3) Remember it's always <u>IN THE HOUSE</u> (→) and then <u>UP THE STAIRS</u> (↑)
   so it's <u>ALONG first</u> and <u>then UP</u>, i.e. x-coordinate first, and then y-coordinate.

The Midpoint of a Line 🏅4

The '<u>MIDPOINT OF A LINE SEGMENT</u>' is the <u>**POINT THAT'S BANG IN THE MIDDLE**</u> of it.

Finding the coordinates of a midpoint is pretty easy.
<u>**LEARN THESE THREE STEPS**</u>...

> 1) Find the <u>average</u> of the <u>x-coordinates</u>.
> 2) Find the <u>average</u> of the <u>y-coordinates</u>.
> 3) Plonk them in <u>brackets</u>.

Midpoint of Jeff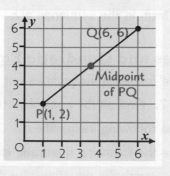

EXAMPLE: P and Q have coordinates (1, 2) and (6, 6).
Find the <u>midpoint</u> of the line PQ.

Average of x-coordinates = $\dfrac{1+6}{2}$ = 3.5

Average of y-coordinates = $\dfrac{2+6}{2}$ = 4

Coordinates of midpoint = (3.5, 4)

But what if you live in a bungalow...

Learn the 3 points for getting x and y the right way round and then try these questions.

Q1   a) Plot point A(–3, 2) and point B(3, 5) on a grid.   [2 marks] 🏅1

     b) Find the coordinates of the midpoint of AB.   [2 marks] 🏅4

Straight-Line Graphs

If you thought I-spy was a fun game, wait 'til you play 'recognise the straight-line graph from the equation'.

Vertical and Horizontal lines: 'x = a' and 'y = a'

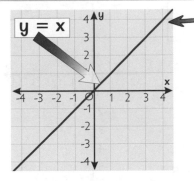

x = a is a <u>vertical line</u> through 'a' on the x-axis

y = a is a <u>horizontal line</u> through 'a' on the y-axis

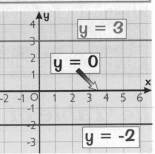

The Main Diagonals: 'y = x' and 'y = –x'

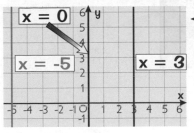

'y = x' is the <u>main diagonal</u> that goes <u>UPHILL</u> from left to right.

'y = -x' is the <u>main diagonal</u> that goes <u>DOWNHILL</u> from left to right.

Other Lines Through the Origin: 'y = ax' and 'y = –ax'

y = ax and y = -ax are the equations for **A SLOPING LINE THROUGH THE ORIGIN.**

The value of '<u>a</u>' (known as the <u>gradient</u>) tells you the steepness of the line. The bigger 'a' is, the steeper the slope. A <u>MINUS SIGN</u> tells you it slopes <u>DOWNHILL</u>.

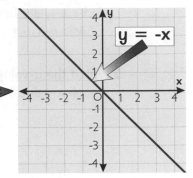

Learn to Spot Straight Lines from their Equations

All straight-line equations just contain '<u>something x</u>, <u>something y</u> and <u>a number</u>'.

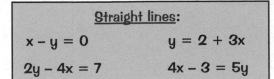

Straight lines:	
$x - y = 0$	$y = 2 + 3x$
$2y - 4x = 7$	$4x - 3 = 5y$

NOT straight lines:	
$y = x^3 + 3$	$\frac{1}{y} + \frac{1}{x} = 2$
$x^2 = 4 - y$	$xy + 3 = 0$

There's more on x^2 graphs on page 48.

It's no Shakespeare, but my favourite line's y = 3x...

It's definitely worth learning all the graphs above. Once you've done that, test yourself with this question.

Q1　On a grid with x-axis from –5 to 5 and y-axis from –5 to 5, draw these lines:
　　a) $y = -1$　　b) $y = -x$　　c) $x = 2$　　　　　　　　　[3 marks]

Drawing Straight-Line Graphs

You might be asked to <u>DRAW THE GRAPH</u> of an equation in the exam.
This <u>EASY METHOD</u> will net you the marks every time:

> 1) Choose <u>3 values of x</u> and <u>draw up a wee table</u>.
> 2) <u>Work out the corresponding y-values</u>.
> 3) <u>Plot the coordinates</u>, and <u>draw the line</u>.

You might get lucky and be <u>given</u> a table in an exam question. Don't worry if it contains <u>5 or 6 values</u>.

Doing the 'Table of Values' (3)

EXAMPLE: Draw the graph of $y = 2x - 3$ for values of x from −2 to 4.

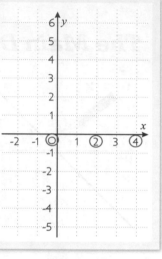

1. Choose 3 easy x-values for your table:
   Use x-values from the grid you're given.
   Avoid negative ones if you can.

x	0	2	4
y			

2. <u>Find the y-values</u> by putting each x-value into the equation:

x	0	2	4
y	−3	1	5

When $x = 0$,
$y = 2x - 3$
$= (2 \times 0) - 3 = -3$

When $x = 4$,
$y = 2x - 3$
$= (2 \times 4) - 3 = 5$

Plotting the Points and Drawing the Graph (3)

EXAMPLE: ...continued from above.

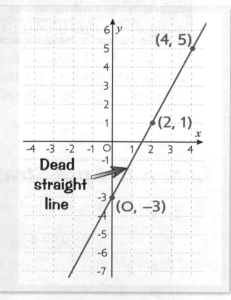

3. <u>PLOT EACH PAIR</u> of x- and y- values from your table.
   The table gives the coordinates (0, −3), (2, 1) and (4, 5).

   Now draw a <u>STRAIGHT LINE</u> through your points.

   > If one point looks a bit wacky, check 2 things:
   > – the <u>y-values</u> you worked out in the table
   > – that you've <u>plotted</u> the points properly.

Careful plotting — the key to straight lines and world domination...

If the examiners are feeling mean, they'll give you an equation like $3x + y = 5$ to plot, making finding the y-values a tad trickier. Just substitute the x-value and find the y-value that makes the equation true.
E.g. when $x = 1$, $3x + y = 5$ → $(3 \times 1) + y = 5$ → $3 + y = 5$ → $y = 2$.

Q1   Draw the graph of $y = x + 4$ for values of x from −6 to 2.   [3 marks] (3)

Q2   Draw the graph of $y + 3x = 2$ for values of x from −2 to 2.   [3 marks] (3)

Straight-Line Graphs — Gradients

Time to hit the slopes. Well, find them anyway...

Finding the Gradient

The <u>gradient</u> of a line is a measure of its <u>slope</u>. The <u>bigger</u> the number, the <u>steeper</u> the line.

EXAMPLE: Find the gradient of the straight line shown.

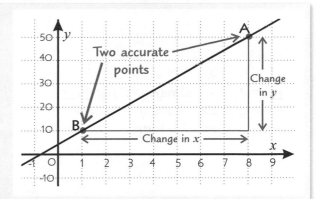

1. Find <u>two accurate points</u> and complete the triangle.

   Choose easy points with positive coordinates.

   Two points that can be read accurately are:

   Point A: (8, 50)   Point B: (1, 10)

2. Find the <u>change in y</u> and the <u>change in x</u>.

   Change in y = 50 − 10 = <u>40</u>

   Change in x = 8 − 1 = <u>7</u>

   Make sure you subtract the x-coordinates the <u>SAME WAY ROUND</u> as you do the y-coordinates.
   E.g. y-coord. of pt A − y-coord. of pt B and x-coord. of pt A − x-coord. of pt B

3. <u>LEARN</u> this formula, and use it:

   $$\text{GRADIENT} = \frac{\text{CHANGE IN Y}}{\text{CHANGE IN X}}$$

   Gradient = $\frac{40}{7}$ = <u>5.71</u> (to 2 d.p.)

   Make sure you get the formula the right way up.
   Remember it's <u>VER</u>y <u>HO</u>t — <u>VER</u>tical over <u>HO</u>rizontal.

4. Check the <u>sign's right</u>.

   If it slopes <u>uphill</u> left → right (⟋) then it's <u>positive</u>.
   If it slopes <u>downhill</u> left → right (⟍) then it's <u>negative</u>.

   As the graph goes uphill, the gradient is <u>positive</u>. So the gradient is <u>5.71</u> (not -5.71).

1) In real life, <u>gradients</u> are often given as a <u>ratio</u> or a <u>percentage</u>.

2) You'll often see them on <u>road signs</u> to describe the <u>steepness</u> of hills and slopes.

3) E.g. if the <u>gradient</u> = $\frac{1}{4}$, it has a ratio of <u>1:4</u>, a percentage of <u>25%</u> and you say it's "<u>1 in 4</u>" (for every 4 units you move horizontally, you move 1 unit vertically).

Finding gradients is often an uphill battle...

Learn the four steps for finding a gradient then have a bash at this Exam Practice Question. Take care — you might not be able to pick two points with nice, positive coordinates. Fun times ahoy.

Q1   Find the gradient of the line shown.   [2 marks]

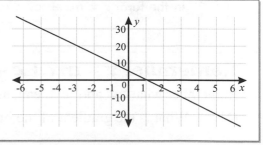

Straight-Line Graphs — y = mx + c

This sounds a bit scary, but give it a go and you might like it.

y = mx + c is the Equation of a Straight Line

y = mx + c is the general equation for a straight-line graph, and you need to remember:

> 'm' is equal to the <u>GRADIENT</u> of the graph
>
> 'c' is the value <u>WHERE IT CROSSES THE Y-AXIS</u> and is called the <u>Y-INTERCEPT</u>.

'<u>m</u>' and '<u>c</u>' are always just <u>numbers</u> — so y = 3x – 1 and y = –x + 2 are in y = mx + c form. →

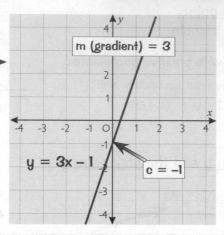

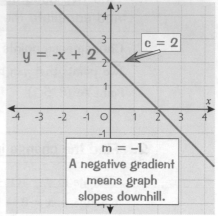

You might have to <u>rearrange</u> a straight-line equation to get it into this form:

<u>Straight line:</u>		<u>Rearranged into 'y = mx + c'</u>	
y = 2 + 3x	→	y = 3x + 2	(m = 3, c = 2)
x – y = 4	→	y = x – 4	(m = 1, c = –4)
4 – 3x = y	→	y = -3x + 4	(m = –3, c = 4)

<u>WATCH OUT</u>: people mix up 'm' and 'c' when they get something like y = 5 + 2x. Remember, 'm' is the number <u>in front of the 'x'</u> and 'c' is the number <u>on its own</u>.

Finding the Equation of a Straight-Line Graph

EXAMPLE: Find the equation of the line on the graph in the form y = mx + c.

1 Find '<u>m</u>' (gradient) $m = \dfrac{\text{change in } y}{\text{change in } x} = \dfrac{15}{30} = \dfrac{1}{2}$
It's an uphill graph, so the gradient is positive.

2 Read off '<u>c</u>' (y-intercept) c = 15

3 Use these to write the equation in the form y = mx + c. $y = \tfrac{1}{2}x + 15$

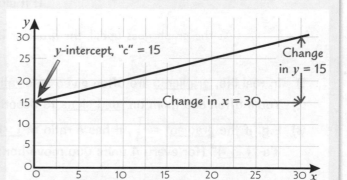

Remember y = mx + c — it'll keep you on the straight and narrow...

Remember what 'm' and 'c' mean, and make sure you've identified them correctly.

Q1   What is the gradient of the line with equation y = 4 – 2x?   [1 mark] (4)

Using y = mx + c

This page covers some of the awkward questions you might get asked about straight lines.

Parallel Lines Have the Same Gradient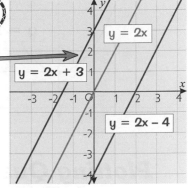

Parallel lines all have the same gradient, which means their
y = mx + c equations all have the same value of m.
So the lines: y = 2x + 3, y = 2x and y = 2x – 4 are all parallel.

EXAMPLE:
Line J has a gradient of –3. Find the equation of Line K, which is parallel to Line J and passes through point (2, 3).

Lines J and K are parallel so their gradients are the same $\Rightarrow$ m = –3

$y = -3x + c$

When $x = 2$, $y = 3$:
$3 = (-3 \times 2) + c \Rightarrow 3 = -6 + c$
$c = 9$

$y = -3x + 9$

1) First find the 'm' value for Line K.
2) Substitute the value for 'm' into y = mx + c to give you the 'equation so far'.
3) Substitute the x and y values for the given point on Line K and solve for 'c'.
4) Write out the full equation.

Finding the Equation of a Line Through Two Points ⑤

If you're given two points on a line you can find the gradient, then you can use the gradient and one of the points to find the equation of the line. It's a bit tricky, but try to follow the method used in this example.

EXAMPLE:
Find the equation of the straight line that passes through (–2, 9) and (3, –1). Give your answer in the form $y = mx + c$.

1) Use the two points to find 'm' (gradient).

$m = \dfrac{\text{change in } y}{\text{change in } x} = \dfrac{-1 - 9}{3 - (-2)} = \dfrac{-10}{5} = -2$

So $y = -2x + c$

2) Substitute one of the points into the equation you've just found.

Substitute (–2, 9) into eqn: $9 = (-2 \times -2) + c$
$9 = 4 + c$

3) Rearrange the equation to find 'c'.

$c = 9 - 4$
$c = 5$

4) Write out the full equation.

$y = -2x + 5$

Sometimes you'll be asked to give your equation in other forms, such as ax + by + c = 0.
Just rearrange your y = mx + c equation to get it in this form. It's no biggie.

Parallel Lines — the sad story of twins that will never meet...

Remember — if two lines are parallel they'll have the same value of m. Run through this page until you're feeling confident with it and then get stuck into this Practice Question:

Q1   a)   Line Q goes through (0, 5) and (4, 7).
          Find the equation of Line Q in the form $y = mx + c$.   [3 marks] ⑤
     b)   Line R is parallel to line Q. It intersects the y-axis at (0, 10).
          Write down the equation of line R in the form $y = mx + c$.   [1 mark] ⑤

Quadratic Graphs

Enough of straight lines. You now get to move on to lovely, smooth curves. Quadratic ones to be precise.

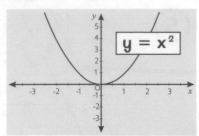

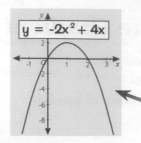

Quadratic graphs are of the form $\underline{y = \text{anything with } x^2}$ (but not higher powers of x).

They all have the same <u>symmetrical</u> bucket shape.

If the x^2 bit has a '–' in front of it then the bucket is <u>upside down</u>.

Plotting Quadratics **(GRADE 5)**

EXAMPLE: Complete the table of values for the equation $y = x^2 + 2x - 3$ and then plot the graph.

x	-4	-3	-2	-1	0	1	2
y	5	0	-3	-4	-3	0	5

1) Substitute each <u>x-value</u> into the equation to get each <u>y-value</u>.

   E.g. $y = (-4)^2 + (2 \times -4) - 3 = 5$

2) Plot the points and join them with a <u>completely smooth curve</u>.

   <u>NEVER EVER</u> let one point drag your graph off in some ridiculous direction. When a graph is generated from an equation, you never get spikes or lumps.

This point is obviously wrong

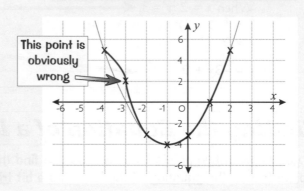

Finding the Turning Point **(GRADE 5)**

You could be asked to find the turning point of a quadratic, so here's a nifty method to do just that.

EXAMPLE: Plot the graph of the equation $y = -x^2 - x + 2$, labelling its turning point with its coordinates.

x	-3	-2	-1	0	1	2
y	-4	0	2	2	0	-4

Plot the graph, then use <u>symmetry</u> to find the turning point of the curve:

1) Choose <u>two points</u> on the curve where the y-value is the <u>same</u>.

   At $x = -1$ and $x = 0$, $y = 2$

2) The <u>x-coordinate</u> of the turning point is <u>halfway</u> between these two values.

   x-coordinate of the turning point = –0.5

3) Put the x-coordinate <u>back</u> into the equation to find the <u>y-coordinate</u>.

   $y = -(-0.5)^2 - (-0.5) + 2$
   $= 2.25$

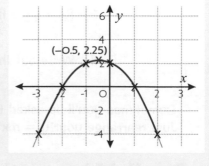

(–0.5, 2.25)

The turning point is (–0.5, 2.25).

How refreshing — a page on graphs. Not seen one of those lately...

You know the deal — learn what's on this page, then treat yourself to answering the question below.

Q1   a) Draw the graph of $y = x^2 + 3x - 7$ for values of x between –3 and 3.   [4 marks] **(GRADE 5)**
     b) Find the turning point of the graph $y = x^2 + 3x - 7$.   [2 marks]

Harder Graphs

Graphs come in all sorts of shapes, sizes and wiggles — here are just a couple:

x^3 (Cubic) Graphs

1) Cubic graphs have the form $y = $ anything with x^3 (but no higher powers of x).

2) All x^3 graphs have a wiggle in the middle.

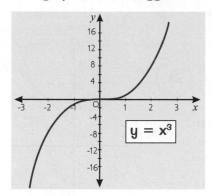

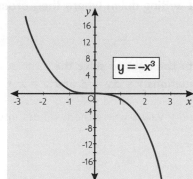

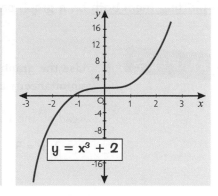

EXAMPLE:

Draw the graph of $y = -x^3 - 10$
for values of x between -3 and $+2$.

Start by making a table of values.

x	-3	-2	-1	0	1	2
$y = -x^3 - 10$	17	-2	-9	-10	-11	-18

E.g. $y = -(-2)^3 - 10 = -2$

Plot the points and join them with a lovely smooth curve.
Don't use your ruler — that would be a trifle daft.

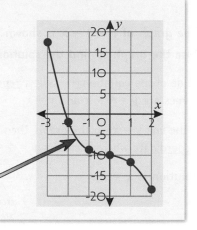

1/x (Reciprocal) Graphs

These appear as two symmetrical curves — one in the top right,
one in the bottom left. They never touch the axes.

They're symmetrical about the lines $y = x$ and $y = -x$.

> If you're not sure what a graph is supposed to look
> like in the exam, remember you can always use a
> table of values — even if it's just to refresh your memory.

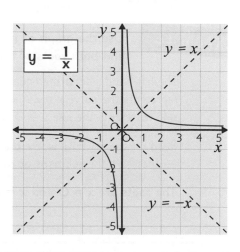

Re-sip-rocal? I didn't like drinking 'rocal' the first time around...

Try covering up the page and drawing the general shape of some cubics and reciprocals. If you're feeling
daring, you could try drawing some of your own equations. When you've finished, have a go at this:

Q1   Draw the graph of $y = x^3 + 8$ from $x = -2$ to $x = 2$.   [4 marks] (5)

Solving Equations Using Graphs

You can plot graphs to find <u>solutions</u> (or <u>approximate</u> solutions) to simultaneous equations and other equations. Plot the equations you want to solve and the solution lies where the lines <u>intersect</u>.

Solving Simultaneous Equations

See p.39 for more on simultaneous equations.

If you want to <u>solve</u> a pair of simultaneous equations with a graph, it's just a matter of <u>plotting them both</u> on a graph and writing down where they cross.

EXAMPLES:

1. Use the graph to the right to solve the simultaneous equations $y = 3x - 3$ and $y = x + 1$.

Read off the x and y values where the two lines intersect.

$x = 2$, $y = 3$

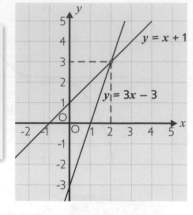

2. The graph of $y = 4 - x$ is shown to the right. Use the graph to find the solution to $4 - x = x$.

Each side of the equation $4 - x = x$ <u>represents a line</u>. These lines are $y = 4 - x$ and $y = x$.

Draw the line $y = x$ on the graph, then read off the <u>x-coordinate</u> where it crosses $y = 4 - x$.

The solution is $x = 2$.

At the point where the lines cross, both sides of the equation are equal, so this is the <u>solution</u>.

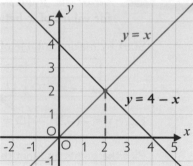

Solving Quadratic Equations

EXAMPLE: Use the graph of $y = 2x^2 - 3x$ (on the right) to find both roots of the equation $2x^2 - 3x = 0$.

The left-hand side of the equation $2x^2 - 3x = 0$ represents the curve $y = 2x^2 - 3x$, and the right-hand side represents the line $y = 0$ (the <u>x-axis</u>).

Read off the <u>x-values</u> where the curve <u>crosses</u> the x-axis — these are the solutions or <u>roots</u>.

The roots are $x = 0$ and $x = 1.5$.

Quadratic equations usually have <u>2 roots</u> (see p.38).

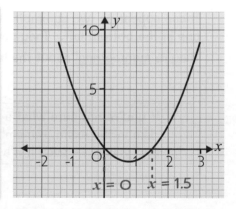

What do you call a giraffe with no eyes? A graph...

Get your graph-plotting pencils ready and have a go at this Practice Question:

Q1 By plotting the graph, find the solutions to the equations $y = 2x - 4$ and $y = x + 2$. [4 marks]

Q2 Using the quadratic graph above, estimate the solutions to $2x^2 - 3x = 6$. [2 marks]

Distance-Time Graphs

Ah, what could be better than some nice D/T graphs? OK, so a slap-up meal with Hugh Jackman might be better. Unfortunately this section isn't called 'Tea With The Stars' so a D/T graph will have to do...

Distance-Time Graphs (3)

Distance-time graphs can look a bit awkward at first, but they're not too bad once you get your head around them.

Just remember these 4 important points:

1) At any point, GRADIENT = SPEED.
2) The STEEPER the graph, the FASTER it's going.
3) FLAT SECTIONS are where it is STOPPED.
4) If the gradient's negative, it's COMING BACK.

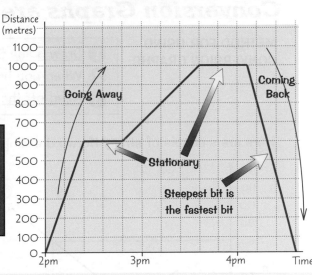

EXAMPLE: Henry went out for a ride on his bike. After a while he got a puncture and stopped to fix it. This graph shows the first part of Henry's journey.

a) What time did Henry leave home?

He left home at the point where the line starts. **At 8:15**

b) How far did Henry cycle before getting a puncture?

The horizontal part of the graph is where Henry stopped. **12 km**

c) What was Henry's speed before getting a puncture?

Using the speed formula (p.69) is the same as finding the gradient.

$$speed = \frac{distance}{time} = \frac{12\,km}{0.5\,hours} = 24\,km/h$$

d) At 9:30 Henry turns round and cycles home at 24 km/h. Complete the graph to show this.

You have to work out how long it will take Henry to cycle the 18 km home:

$$time = \frac{distance}{speed} = \frac{18\,km}{24\,km/h} = 0.75\,hours$$

$$0.75 \times 60\,mins = 45\,mins$$

Decimal times are yuck, so convert it to minutes.

45 minutes after 9:30 is 10:15, so that's the time Henry gets home. Now you can complete the graph.

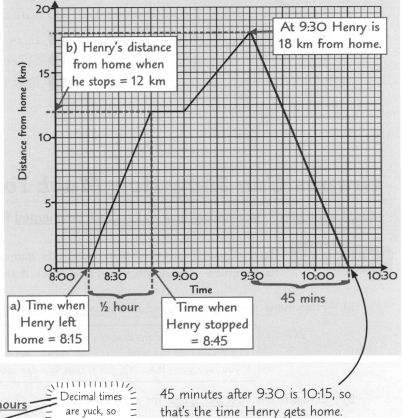

D-T Graphs — filled with highs and lows...

... like my bungee jumping career. The only way to get good at distance-time graphs is to get some practice.

Q1 a) Using the graph above, how long did Henry stop for? [1 mark] (3)

b) What was Henry's speed after he had repaired the puncture, before he turned back home? [2 marks] (3)

Real-Life Graphs

In the exam you might get a graph which converts something like <u>£ to dollars</u> or <u>mph to km/h</u>.

Conversion Graphs are Easy to Use ②

METHOD FOR USING CONVERSION GRAPHS:

① <u>Draw a line</u> from a value on <u>one axis</u>.

② When you hit the LINE, <u>change direction</u> and go straight to <u>the other axis</u>.

③ <u>Read off the value</u> from this axis. The two values are <u>equivalent</u>.

Here are a couple of straightforward examples: <u>This graph converts between miles and kilometres</u>

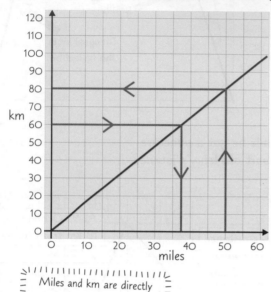

miles

Miles and km are directly proportional. See p.58-59.

EXAMPLE: How many miles is 60 km?

① Draw a line <u>across</u> from '60' on the '<u>km' axis</u>.

② When it <u>hits the line</u>, go <u>down</u> to the 'miles' axis.

③ Read off the answer:

37.5 miles

EXAMPLE: How many km is 150 miles? ③

150 miles is way off the graph, so find a point which will make calculating easy. Use 50 miles, then <u>multiply by 3</u>.

① Draw a line <u>up</u> from '50' on the 'miles' axis.

② When it <u>hits the line</u>, go <u>across</u> to the 'km' axis.

③ Read off the answer and <u>multiply by 3</u> to find 150 miles.

80 × 3 = 240 km

Graphs Can Show How Much You'll Pay ③

Graphs are great for showing how much you'll be <u>charged</u> for using a service or buying multiple items.

EXAMPLE: BeyondSpaceInvaders hires out computer games to its members. The graph shows how much it charges.

a) How many games are included in the <u>basic annual cost</u>?

20

The first section of the graph is <u>horizontal</u>. You pay £15 if you rent between 0 and 20 games. It's only if you hire <u>more</u> than 20 games that you pay more.

b) Estimate the <u>cost per game</u> for additional games.

Gradient of sloped section = cost per game

$$\frac{\text{vertical change}}{\text{horizontal change}} = \frac{25}{20} = £1.25 \text{ per game}$$

 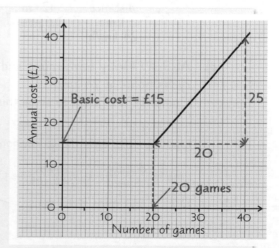

Learn how to convert graph questions into marks...

Draw your conversion lines on the graph in the exam. If all else fails, this might get you a mark.

Q1 The distance between Tokyo and London is 6000 miles.

Use the graph at the top of the page to estimate this distance in km. [2 marks] ③

Real-Life Graphs

Graphs can tell you just about anything. I can't show you all the possibilities due to health and safety concerns about back injuries resulting from the weight of the book. But here are some useful examples.

Gradients Show the Rate of Change

Basically, gradients always show you the 'change in something per something else'.

The gradient is always **(y-axis UNITS) PER (x-axis UNITS)**

The graph below shows the distance travelled by a remote control car.

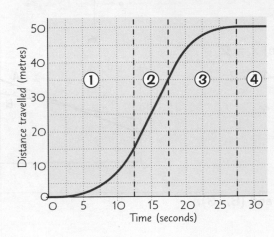

The <u>gradient</u> of the <u>graph</u> tells you the <u>speed</u> of the remote control car (see p.51).

① In this section of the graph the gradient is <u>increasing</u> (i.e. the graph is getting steeper) so the speed of the car is increasing — it's <u>accelerating</u>.

② Here, the gradient doesn't change so the car is travelling at a <u>constant speed</u>.

③ The gradient is <u>decreasing</u> (i.e. the graph is getting flatter) so the speed of the car is decreasing — it's <u>decelerating</u>.

④ The gradient is flat so the car has <u>stopped</u>.

Graphs Can Show Changes with Time

EXAMPLE: Four different-shaped glasses are shown on the right. Juice is poured into each glass at a <u>constant rate</u>.

Each graph below shows how the height of juice in one glass changes. Match each graph to the correct glass.

 A <u>steeper</u> slope means that the juice height is changing <u>faster</u>.

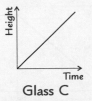 **Glass C**
 Glass B
 Glass D
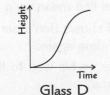 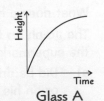 **Glass A**

Glass C has <u>straight vertical sides</u>, so the juice height increases steadily.

Glass B is <u>widest at the bottom</u>, so the juice height increases <u>slowly at first</u>.

Glass D is <u>narrowest in the middle</u>, so the height will increase <u>fastest</u> in the <u>middle part</u> of the graph.

Glass A is <u>narrowest at the bottom</u>, so the height will increase <u>fastest</u> at the start of the graph.

Exam marks per unit of brainpower...

There's loads to take in on this page — keep reading through it until you're happy with it, then try this:

Q1   A bath is being filled using only the hot tap. After 3 minutes the cold tap is also turned on. Which graph, A or B, shows how the depth of water in the bath changes over time?

[1 mark]

Revision Questions for Section Three

Well, that wraps up <u>Section Three</u> — time to put yourself to the test and find out <u>how much you really know</u>.

- Try these questions and <u>tick off each one</u> when you <u>get it right</u>.
- When you've done <u>all the questions</u> for a topic and are <u>completely happy</u> with it, tick off the topic.

<u>Coordinates and Midpoints (p42)</u> ☑

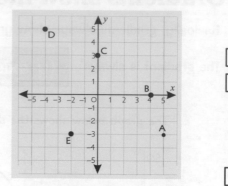

1) Give the coordinates of points A to E in the diagram on the right. ☑

2) Find the midpoint of a line segment with endpoints B and C. ☑

<u>Straight-Line Graphs (p43-47)</u> ☑

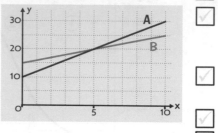

3) Draw these lines on a grid: a) y = –x, b) y = –4, c) x = 2 ☑

4) By making a table of values, draw the graph of y = –4x – 2. ☑

5) a) Find the gradient of line A on the right.
   b) Find the equation of line B on the right, giving your answer in the form y = mx + c. ☑

6) Find the equation of the line passing through (4, 2) which is parallel to y = 2x – 1. ☑

7) Find the equation of the line passing through (3, -6) and (6, -3). ☑

<u>Quadratic and Harder Graphs (p48-50)</u> ☑

8) Describe the shapes of the graphs $y = x^2 – 8$ and $y = –x^2 + 2$. ☑

9) a) Create and complete a table of values for values of x between –3 and 1 for the equation $y = x^2 + 3x$.
   b) Plot the graph of $y = x^2 + 3x$, labelling the turning point of the curve with its coordinates. ☑

10) Describe <u>in words</u> and with a sketch the forms of these graphs:
    a) $y = ax^3$ b) $y = 1/x$ ☑

11) Plot the graph y = 2x – 1 and use it to find the solution to 5 = 2x – 1. ☑

<u>Distance-Time Graphs (p51)</u> ☑

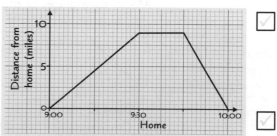

12) What does a horizontal line mean on a distance-time graph? ☑

13) The graph on the right shows Ben's car journey to the supermarket and home again.
    a) Did he drive faster on his way to the supermarket or on his way home?
    b) How long did he spend at the supermarket? ☑

<u>Real-Life Graphs (p52-53)</u> ☑

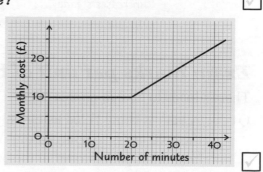

14) On a straight-line graph, how would you find the rate of change? ☑

15) This graph shows the monthly cost of a mobile phone contract.
    a) How many minutes does the basic monthly fee include?
    b) Mary uses her phone for 35 minutes one month. What will her bill be?
    c) Stuart is charged £14 one month. Estimate how long he used his phone for.
    d) Estimate the cost per minute for additional minutes. Give your answer to the nearest 1p. ☑

Ratios

Ratios are a pretty important topic — they can crop up in all sorts of questions, so you need to be prepared. If you understand the examples on the next three pages, you'll have a fighting chance in the exams.

Reducing Ratios to their Simplest Form

To reduce a ratio to a <u>simpler form</u>, divide <u>all the numbers</u> in the ratio by the <u>same thing</u> (a bit like simplifying a fraction — see p.12). It's in its <u>simplest form</u> when there's nothing left you can divide by.

> **EXAMPLE:** Write the ratio 15:18 in its simplest form.
>
> For the ratio 15:18, both numbers have a <u>factor</u> of 3, so <u>divide them by 3</u>. $\div 3 \left(\dfrac{15:18}{= \ 5:6} \right) \div 3$
>
> We can't reduce this any further. So the simplest form of 15:18 is **5:6**.

A handy trick for the calculator papers — use the fraction button

If you enter a fraction with the ⬚/⬚ or a^b/c button, the calculator automatically cancels it down when you press ⚬.

So for the ratio 8:12, just enter $\dfrac{8}{12}$ as a fraction, and you'll get the reduced fraction $\dfrac{2}{3}$.

Now you just change it back to ratio form, i.e. <u>2 : 3</u>. Ace.

The More Awkward Cases:

1) If the ratio contains <u>decimals</u> or <u>fractions</u> — <u>multiply</u>

> For fractions, multiply by a number that gets rid of both <u>denominators</u>.

> **EXAMPLE:** Simplify the ratio 2.4:3.6 as far as possible.
>
> 1) <u>Multiply both sides by 10</u> to get rid of the decimal parts.
> 2) Now <u>divide</u> to reduce the ratio to its simplest form.
>
> $\begin{aligned} &\times 10 \left(\dfrac{2.4:3.6}{24:36} \right) \times 10 \\ = \ &\div 12 \left(\right) \div 12 \\ = \ &\qquad 2:3 \end{aligned}$

2) If the ratio has <u>mixed units</u> — convert to the <u>smaller unit</u>

> **EXAMPLE:** Reduce the ratio 24 mm:7.2 cm to its simplest form.
>
> 1) <u>Convert</u> 7.2 cm to millimetres.
> 2) <u>Simplify</u> the resulting ratio. Once the units on both sides are the same, <u>get rid of them</u> for the final answer.
>
> 24 mm:7.2 cm
> = 24 mm:72 mm
> $= \ \div 24 \searrow 1:3 \swarrow \div 24$

I ain't gettin' on no gosh-darned plane!

Don't be so awkward, case.

3) To get to the form <u>1 : n</u> or <u>n : 1</u> — just <u>divide</u>

> **EXAMPLE:** Reduce 5:54 to the form 1:n.
>
> Divide both sides by 5:
>
> $\div 5 \left(\dfrac{5:54}{= \ 1: \dfrac{54}{5}} \right) \div 5$ or 1:10.8

The simpler the ratio the better as far as I'm concerned...

Whole number ratios are easy to simplify, but you need to make sure you can do the awkward cases too.

Q1   Simplify: a) 25:35   b) $\dfrac{9}{4} : \dfrac{15}{2}$ c) 8:18 to the form 1:n   [4 marks]

Ratios

Another page on ratios coming up — it's more interesting than the first but not as exciting as the next one...

Scaling Up Ratios

If you know the ratio between parts and the actual size of one part, you can scale the ratio up to find the other parts.

> **EXAMPLE:** Mortar is made from mixing sand and cement in the ratio 7:2. How many buckets of mortar will be made if 21 buckets of sand are used in the mixture?
>
> You need to multiply by 3 to go from 7 to 21 on the left-hand side (LHS) — so do that to both sides:
>
> So 21 buckets of sand and 6 buckets of cement are used.
>
> sand:cement
>
> $\times 3 \left(\begin{array}{c} 7:2 \\ 21:6 \end{array} \right) \times 3$
>
> Amount of mortar made = 21 + 6 = 27 buckets

The two parts of a ratio are always in direct proportion (see p.58-59). So in the example above, sand and cement are in direct proportion, e.g. if the amount of sand doubles, the amount of cement doubles.

Writing Ratios as Fractions

1) To write one part as a fraction of another part — put one number over the other.

E.g. if apples and oranges are in the ratio 2:9 then we say there are $\frac{2}{9}$ as many apples as oranges or $\frac{9}{2}$ times as many oranges as apples.

2) To write one part as a fraction of the total — add up the parts to find the total, then put the part you want over the total.

E.g. a pie dough is made by mixing flour, butter and water in the ratio 3:2:1.
The total number of parts is $3 + 2 + 1 = \underline{6}$.
So $\frac{3}{6} = \frac{1}{2}$ of the dough is flour, $\frac{2}{6} = \frac{1}{3}$ is butter and $\frac{1}{6}$ is water.

Part : Whole Ratios

You might come across a ratio where the LHS is included in the RHS — these are called part:whole ratios.

> **EXAMPLE:** Mrs Miggins owns tabby cats and ginger cats.
> The ratio of tabby cats to the total number of cats is 3:5.
>
> **a)** What fraction of Mrs Miggins' cats are tabby cats?
>
> The ratio tells you that for every 5 cats, 3 are tabby cats. $\quad \frac{part}{whole} = \frac{3}{5}$
>
> **b)** What is the ratio of tabby cats to ginger cats?
>
> 3 in every 5 cats are tabby, so 2 in every 5 are ginger.
>
> $5 - 3 = 2$
>
> For every 3 tabby cats there are 2 ginger cats.
>
> tabby:ginger = 3:2
>
> **c)** Mrs Miggins has 12 tabby cats. How many ginger cats does she have?
>
> Scale up the ratio from part b) to find the number of ginger cats.
>
> tabby:ginger
>
> $\times 4 \left(\begin{array}{c} 3:2 \\ 12:8 \end{array} \right) \times 4$
>
> There are 8 ginger cats

Ratios

If you were worried I was running out of <u>great stuff</u> to say about ratios then worry no more...

Proportional Division

In a <u>proportional division</u> question a <u>TOTAL AMOUNT</u> is split into parts <u>in a certain ratio</u>.
The key word here is <u>PARTS</u> — concentrate on 'parts' and it all becomes quite painless:

> **EXAMPLE:** Jess, Mo and Greg share £9100 in the ratio 2:4:7. How much does Mo get?
>
> 1) <u>ADD UP THE PARTS</u>:
>   The ratio 2:4:7 means there will be a total of 13 <u>parts</u>:   2 + 4 + 7 = 13 parts
>
> 2) <u>DIVIDE TO FIND ONE "PART"</u>:
>   Just divide the <u>total amount</u> by the number of <u>parts</u>:   £9100 ÷ 13 = £700   (= 1 part)
>
> 3) <u>MULTIPLY TO FIND THE AMOUNTS</u>:
>   We want to know <u>Mo's share</u>, which is <u>4 parts</u>:   4 parts = 4 × £700 = £2800

Watch out for pesky proportional division questions that <u>don't</u> give you the <u>total amount</u>.
You can't just follow the method above, you'll have to be a bit more <u>crafty</u>.

> **EXAMPLE:** A baguette is cut into 3 pieces. The second piece is twice as long
> as the first and the third piece is five times as long as the first.
>
> a) Find the ratio of the lengths of the 3 pieces. Give your answer in its simplest form.
>
>   If the **first piece** is 1 part, then the **second piece** is 1 × 2 = 2 parts
>   and the **third piece** is 1 × 5 = 5 parts. So the **ratio of the lengths = 1:2:5**.
>
> b) The first piece is 28 cm smaller than the third piece. How long is the second piece?
>
>   1) Work out <u>how many parts</u> 28 cm makes up.   28 cm = 3rd piece − 1st piece
>   = 5 parts − 1 part = 4 parts
>
>   2) <u>Divide</u> to find <u>one part</u>.   28 cm ÷ 4 = 7 cm
>
>   3) <u>Multiply</u> to find the length of the <u>2nd piece</u>.   2nd piece = 2 parts = 2 × 7 cm = **14 cm**

Ratio Nelson — he proportionally divided the French at Trafalgar...

There's loads of stuff to learn about ratios, so have another look over it and then try these questions:

Q1   Orange squash is made of water and concentrate in the ratio 11:2.
  a) What fraction of the squash is made up from concentrate?   [1 mark]
  b) How many litres of water are needed if 6 litres of concentrate are used?   [1 mark]

Q2   The ages of Ben, Graham and Pam are in the ratio 5:3:1.
  Their combined age is 108. How old is Graham?   [2 marks] (4)

Q3   Square A has an area of 36 cm². The areas of square A and square B are
  in the ratio 4:9. What is the side length of square B?   [2 marks] (4)

Q4   In an office, the ratio of people who drink tea to people who drink coffee is 8:5.
  18 more people drink tea than coffee. How many people drink coffee?   [3 marks]

Direct Proportion Problems

Direct proportion problems all involve amounts that <u>increase</u> or <u>decrease</u> together. Awww.

Learn the Golden Rule for Proportion Questions

There are lots of exam questions which at first sight seem completely different but in fact they can all be done using the <u>GOLDEN RULE</u>...

DIVIDE FOR ONE, THEN TIMES FOR ALL

My favourite cereal is muesli.

EXAMPLE: 5 pints of milk cost £1.30. How much will 3 pints cost?

The <u>GOLDEN RULE</u> tells you to:
<u>Divide the price by 5</u> to find how much <u>FOR ONE PINT</u>,
then <u>multiply by 3</u> to find how much <u>FOR 3 PINTS</u>.

1 pint: £1.30 ÷ 5 = 0.26 = 26p

3 pints: 26p × 3 = 78p

EXAMPLE: Emma is handing out some leaflets. She gets paid per leaflet she hands out.
If she hands out 300 leaflets she gets £2.40.
How many leaflets will she have to hand out to earn £8.50?

<u>Divide by £2.40</u> to find how many leaflets she has to hand out to earn <u>£1</u>.

To earn £1: 300 ÷ £2.40 = 125 leaflets

<u>Multiply by £8.50</u> to find how many leaflets she has to hand out to earn <u>£8.50</u>.

To earn £8.50: 125 × £8.50 = 1062.5

So she'll need to hand out **1063** leaflets.

You need to round your answer up because 1062 wouldn't be enough.

Scaling Recipes Up or Down

EXAMPLE: Judy is making orange and pineapple punch using the recipe shown on the right.
She wants to make enough to serve 20 people.
How much of each ingredient will Judy need?

<u>Fruit Punch (serves 8)</u>
800 ml orange juice
140 g fresh pineapple

The <u>GOLDEN RULE</u> tells you to <u>divide each amount by 8</u> to find how much <u>FOR ONE PERSON</u>, then <u>multiply by 20</u> to find how much <u>FOR 20 PEOPLE</u>.

So for 1 person you need:

800 ml ÷ 8 = 100 ml orange juice ⇒

140 g ÷ 8 = 17.5 g pineapple ⇒

And for 20 people you need:

20 × 100 ml = 2000 ml orange juice

20 × 17.5 g = 350 g pineapple

The Three Mathsketeers say "divide for one, then times for all"...

The trick here is knowing when to use the golden rule. Only use it when two things are in direct proportion, e.g. when doubling one quantity doubles the other. Learning the examples above will help.

Q1   Seven pencils cost £1.40.   a) How much will four pencils cost?   [2 marks]
          b) What is the maximum number of pencils you could buy for £6.50?   [2 marks]

Q2   It costs £43.20 for 8 people to go on a rollercoaster 6 times.
       How much will it cost for 15 people to go on a rollercoaster 5 times?   [4 marks]

Direct Proportion Problems

Best Buy Questions

A slightly different type of direct proportion question is comparing the 'value for money' of 2 or 3 similar items. For these, follow the second GOLDEN RULE...

> **Divide by the PRICE in pence (to get the amount per penny)**

EXAMPLE: The local 'Supplies 'n' Vittals' stocks two sizes of Jamaican Gooseberry Jam, as shown on the right. Which of these represents better value for money?

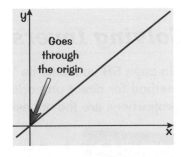

Jamaican Gooseberry Jam 350g

Jamaican Gooseberry Jam 100g

350 g at 80p   100 g at 42p

Follow the GOLDEN RULE —
divide by the price in pence to get the amount per penny.

In the 350 g jar you get   350 g ÷ 80p = 4.38 g per penny
In the 100 g jar you get   100 g ÷ 42p = 2.38 g per penny

The 350 g jar is better value for money, because you get more jam per penny.

In some cases it might be easier to divide by the weight to get the cost per gram.
If you're feeling confident then you can do it this way — if not, the golden rule always works.

Graphing Direct Proportion

> Two things are in direct proportion if, when you plot them on a graph, you get a straight line through the origin.

Remember, the general equation for a straight line through the origin is $y = Ax$ (see p.43) where A is a number.
All direct proportions can be written as an equation in this form.

Goes through the origin

EXAMPLE: The amount of petrol, p litres, a car uses is directly proportional to the distance, d km, that the car travels. The car used 12 litres of petrol on a 160 km journey.

a) Write an equation in the form $p = Ad$ to represent this direct proportion.

1) Put the values of $p = 12$ and $d = 160$ into the equation to find the value of A.

$$12 = A \times 160$$
$$A = \frac{12}{160}$$
$$A = 0.075$$

2) Put the value of A back into the equation.

$$p = 0.075d$$

b) Sketch the graph of this direct proportion, marking two points on the line.

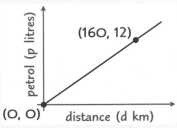

petrol (p litres)

(160, 12)

(0, 0)   distance (d km)

Calm down, you're blowing this page all out of proportion...

A mixed bag on this page — soak it all in and then have a crack at these questions.

Q1 Tomato ketchup comes in bottles of three sizes: 250 g for 50p, 770 g for £1.40 and 1600 g for £3.20. Which bottle represents the best value for money? [3 marks]

Q2 Brass is made by mixing copper and zinc in the ratio 3 : 2 by weight.
 a) Sketch a graph showing the weight of copper against the weight of zinc in a sample of brass. Mark two points on the graph. [3 marks]
 b) What aspects of the graph show that copper and zinc are in direct proportion? [1 mark]

Inverse Proportion Problems

Here's a trickier type of proportion — but once you've learnt this page you'll be an expert.

Graphing Inverse Proportion (4)

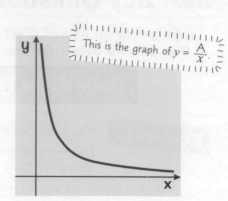

This is the graph of $y = \dfrac{A}{x}$.

> **When two things are in inverse proportion, one increases as the other decreases.**

On the graph you can see that as the value of <u>x increases</u>, the value of <u>y decreases</u>. E.g. if x is <u>doubled</u>, y is <u>halved</u>, or if x is <u>multiplied by 5</u>, y is <u>divided by 5</u>.

The general equation for inverse proportion is $y = \dfrac{A}{x}$.

EXAMPLE: Circle each of the equations below that show that s is inversely proportional to t.

$\boxed{s = \dfrac{3}{t}}$ $9s = t$ $\boxed{t = \dfrac{1}{s}}$ $s = \dfrac{3}{t^2}$ $s = \dfrac{3}{t} + 7$ $\boxed{\dfrac{s}{5} = \dfrac{1}{t}}$

$s = \dfrac{3}{t}$ $s = \dfrac{1}{t}$ $s = \dfrac{5}{t}$

Check which equations can be written in the form $s = \dfrac{A}{t}$.

Solving Inverse Proportion Questions (4)

On page 58 you saw the 'divide and times' method for direct proportions. Well, inverse proportions are the opposite so you have to:

> **TIMES for ONE, then DIVIDE for ALL**

EXAMPLES:

1. It takes 3 farmers 10 hours to plough a field. How long would it take 6 farmers?

<u>Multiply by 3</u> to find how long it would take <u>1 farmer</u>. $10 \times 3 = 30$ hours for 1 farmer

<u>Divide by 6</u> to find how long it would take <u>6 farmers</u>. $30 \div 6 = 5$ hours for 6 farmers

> **Note:** Another way of looking at this question is that there are <u>twice</u> as many farmers, so it will take <u>half</u> as long ($10 \div 2 = 5$ hours).

2. 4 bakers can decorate 100 cakes in 5 hours. If 5 bakers work at the same rate, how much quicker would they decorate 100 cakes?

<u>Multiply by 4</u> to find how long it would take <u>1 baker</u>.   5 hours $\times 4 = 20$ hours for 1 baker

<u>Divide by 5</u> to find how long it would take <u>5 bakers</u>. $20 \div 5 = 4$ hours for 5 bakers

So 5 bakers are $5 - 4 = 1$ hour quicker than 4.

noitroporp — it's an inverse proportion...

You should be able to identify, draw the graph of and solve inverse proportions. Have a go at solving these:

Q1   It takes 2 carpenters 6 hours to make a bookcase.
How long would it take 8 carpenters to make a bookcase?   [2 marks]

Q2   *m* is inversely proportional to *n*.
When $m = 20$, $n = 5$. What is the value of *m* when *n* is 32?   [2 marks]

Percentages

You're going to see <u>6 different types</u> of percentage question on the next three pages.
The first few shouldn't give you too much trouble. Especially if you remember:

1) <u>'Per cent'</u> means <u>'out of 100'</u>, so 20% means '20 out of 100' = $\frac{20}{100}$.

2) To work out the percentage <u>OF</u> something replace the word <u>OF</u> with a <u>multiplication</u> (×).

Six Different Question Types

Type 1 — "Find x% of y"

If you have a <u>calculator</u>, turn the percentage into a <u>decimal</u>, then <u>multiply</u>.

Find the other 50%
of my sandwich

EXAMPLE: Find 18% of £4.

Change 18% to a
<u>decimal</u> and <u>multiply</u>.

18% of £4 → Replace 'of' with '×'.
= 18% × £4
= 0.18 × £4 = £0.72

If you <u>don't have a calculator</u>, you can use this clever method instead:

EXAMPLE: Find 135% of 600 kg.

1) Find <u>10%</u> by <u>dividing by 10</u>:
2) Find <u>5%</u> by <u>dividing 10% by 2</u>:
3) Use these values to <u>make 135%</u>:

100% = 600 kg
10% = 600 ÷ 10 = 60 kg
5% = 60 ÷ 2 = 30 kg
135% = 100% + (3 × 10%) + 5%
= 600 + (3 × 60) + 30 = 810 kg

You can also find 1% by dividing by 100.

Type 2 — "Express x as a percentage of y"

<u>Divide</u> x by y, then multiply by <u>100</u>.

If you don't have a calculator you'll have to simplify the fraction (see p12).

EXAMPLES: 1. Give 36p as a percentage of 80p.

<u>Divide</u> 36p by 80p, <u>then multiply</u> by 100: $\frac{36}{80}$ × 100 = 45%

2. Farmer Littlewood measured the width of his prized pumpkin at the start and end of the month.
At the start of the month it was <u>84 cm</u> wide and at the end of the month it was <u>1.32 m</u> wide.
Give the <u>width at the end</u> of the month <u>as a percentage</u> of the <u>width at the start</u>.

1) Make sure both amounts are in the <u>same units</u>.
2) <u>Divide</u> 132 cm by 84 cm, <u>then multiply</u> by 100:

1.32 m = 132 cm
$\frac{132}{84}$ × 100 = 157.14% (2 d.p.)

Fact: 70% of people understand percentages, the other 40% don't...

It's all fairly straightforward here — just make sure you can do percentages with and without a calculator.

Q1 a) Without using a calculator find 36% of 300. [3 marks]
b) Use a calculator to find 139% of 505. [2 marks]

Q2 A full bottle of pearade holds 1.2 litres. After pouring a glass there is 744 ml left
in the bottle. What percentage of the original amount is left in the bottle? [2 marks]

Percentages

Type 3 — New Amount After a % Increase or Decrease

There are two different ways of finding the new amount after a percentage increase or decrease:

1) Find the % then Add or Subtract.

Find the % of the original amount. Add this on to (or subtract from) the original value.

> **EXAMPLE:** A dress has increased in price by 30%.
> It originally cost £40. What is the new price of the dress?
>
> 1) Find 30% of £40:   30% of £40 = 30% × £40
> 2) It's an increase, so   = 0.3 × 40 = £12
>   add on to the original: £40 + £12 = £52

2) The Multiplier Method

This time, you first need to find the multiplier — the decimal that represents the percentage change.

> E.g. 5% increase is 1.05 (= 1 + 0.05)   26% decrease is 0.74 (= 1 − 0.26)

Then you just multiply the original value by the multiplier and voilà — you have the answer.

> A % decrease has a multiplier less than 1,
> a % increase has a multiplier greater than 1.

> **EXAMPLE:** A hat is reduced in price by 20% in the sales.
> It originally cost £12. What is the new price of the hat?
>
> 1) Find the multiplier: 20% decrease = 1 − 0.20 = 0.8
> 2) Multiply the original value by the multiplier: £12 × 0.8 = £9.60 ← Voilà

Type 4 — Simple Interest

Compound interest is covered on page 65.

Simple interest means a certain percentage of the original amount only is paid at regular intervals (usually once a year). So the amount of interest is the same every time it's paid.

> **EXAMPLE:** Regina invests £380 in an account which pays 3% simple interest each year.
> How much interest will she earn in 4 years?
>
> 1) Work out the amount of interest earned in one year: 3% = 3 ÷ 100 = 0.03
>   3% of £380 = 0.03 × £380 = £11.40
> 2) Multiply by 4 to get the total interest for 4 years: 4 × £11.40 = £45.60

Simple Interest — it's simple, but it's not that interesting...

Another two types of percentages for you here — try the methods out on these practice questions.

Q1   A unicorn costing £4000 is reduced by 15% in a sale. What is its new price?   [2 marks]

Q2   Al puts £110 into a bank account that pays 6% simple interest each year. What will
       his bank balance be after 3 years if he doesn't pay in or take out any money?   [3 marks]

Percentages

Watch out for these <u>trickier types</u> of percentage question — they'll often include lots of real-life context.

Type 5 — Finding the Percentage Change

1) This is the formula for giving a <u>change in value</u> as a <u>percentage</u> — <u>LEARN IT, AND USE IT</u>:

$$\text{PERCENTAGE 'CHANGE'} = \frac{\text{'CHANGE'}}{\text{ORIGINAL}} \times 100$$

2) Typical questions will ask 'Find the percentage <u>increase</u>/<u>profit</u>/<u>error</u>'
   or 'Calculate the percentage <u>decrease</u>/<u>loss</u>/<u>discount</u>', etc.

> **EXAMPLE:** Tariq buys a plain plate for £2. He paints it, then sells it at a craft fair for £3.75.
> Find his profit as a percentage.
>
> 1) Here the 'change' is <u>profit</u>, so the formula looks like this: $\text{percentage profit} = \frac{\text{profit}}{\text{original}} \times 100$
>
> 2) Work out the <u>profit</u> (amount made – original cost). $\text{profit} = £3.75 - £2 = £1.75$
>
> 3) Calculate the <u>percentage</u> profit. $\text{percentage profit} = \frac{£1.75}{£2} \times 100 = 87.5\%$

Type 6 — Finding the Original Value

This is the type that <u>most people get wrong</u> — but only because they
<u>don't recognise</u> it as this type, and don't apply this <u>simple method</u>:

> 1) Write the amount in the question as a <u>percentage of the original value</u>.
> 2) <u>Divide</u> to find <u>1%</u> of the original value.
> 3) <u>Multiply by 100</u> to give the original value (= 100%).

> **EXAMPLE:** A house increases in value by 10% to £165 000.
> Find what it was worth before the rise.
>
> *Note: The <u>new</u>, not the original value is given.*
>
> 1) An <u>increase</u> of 10% means £165 000
>   represents <u>110% of the original</u> value.
>
> 2) Divide by 110 to find <u>1%</u> of the original value.
>
> 3) Then multiply by 100.
>
> ÷110 $\Big($ £165 000 = 110%
>
> £1500 = 1%
>
> ×100 $\Big($ £150 000 = 100%
>
> So the original value was £150 000
>
> *If it was a <u>decrease</u> of 10%, then you'd put '£165 000 = <u>90%</u>' and divide by 90 instead of 110.*

Always set them out <u>exactly like this example</u>. The trickiest bit is deciding the top % figure on the right-hand side — the 2nd and 3rd rows are <u>always</u> 1% and 100%.

The % change in my understanding of this topic is 100%...

The methods above are easy to follow but the questions can be a bit tricky. Try these Practice Questions:

Q1   What is the percentage decrease when 1200 g is decreased to 900 g?   [3 marks]

Q2   A junk shop is having a 20% off sale. A lobster statue is £4.88 in the sale.
How much was the lobster statue before the sale?   [3 marks]

Percentages

This page is all about tackling those percentage questions in your exam. Once you know the different types (pages 61-63), have a look at these examples and try to follow them step by step.

Working with Percentages

1) Sometimes there isn't a set method you can follow to answer percentage questions.

2) You'll have to use what you've learnt on the last few pages and do a bit of thinking for yourself.

EXAMPLES:

1. 80% of the members of a gym are male.
35% of the male members are aged 40 and over.
What percentage of gym members are males under 40 years old?

> It's just like finding x% of y — but this time the y is a percentage too.

1) The percentage of male members under 40 is: $100\% - 35\% = 65\%$

2) The percentage of gym members that are male and under 40 is: 65% of $80\% = 0.65 \times 80\%$ $= 52\%$

2. Yohan sells scarves. Each scarf costs £1.50 to make. One day he sold 500 scarves. He sold 90% of them for £2 each and the rest at £1 each. How much profit did Yohan make?

1) To make 500 scarves, it costs him: $500 \times £1.50 = £750$

2) Work out how many were sold at each price. 90% of $500 = 0.9 \times 500 = 450$ at £2 each
10% of $500 = 0.1 \times 500 = 50$ at £1 each

3) Work out the amount he made from selling them. $(450 \times £2) + (50 \times £1) = £900 + £50 = £950$

4) Calculate his profit. $£950 - £750 = £200$

3. The number of visitors to a theme park in 2012 was 250 000. In 2013, the number of visitors was 12% lower than in 2012. In 2014, the number of visitors was 15% higher than in 2013. How many visitors were there in 2014?

1) First, work out the number of visitors in 2013. $100\% - 12\% = 88\%$
88% of $250\,000 = 0.88 \times 250\,000 = 220\,000$

2) Then work out the number of visitors in 2014. Make sure you use the value you've just found. $100\% + 15\% = 115\%$
115% of $220\,000 = 1.15 \times 220\,000 = 253\,000$

Practise percentages for practically perfect preparation... pineapple

If an examiner is feeling especially awful, they'll throw a tougher percentage question at you. Just use what you know about percentages to work through it step-by-step. Test your skills with these questions:

Q1 One day at a school 70% of the students wore a polo shirt.
80% of the students wearing polo shirts were boys.
What percentage of students were boys who wore polo shirts? [2 marks]

Q2 In May a bookshop sold 1600 books. 45% more books were sold in June than in May.
15% fewer books were sold in July than in June.
a) Find the number of books the bookshop sold in: i) June ii) July [2 marks]
b) What is the percentage increase in sales from May to July? [3 marks]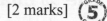

Compound Growth and Decay

One more sneaky % type for you... In <u>compound growth/decay</u> the amount added on/taken away <u>changes</u> each time — it's a percentage of the <u>new amount</u>, rather than the <u>original amount</u>.

Compound Growth and Decay

<u>Compound interest</u> is a popular context for these questions — it means the interest is <u>added on each time</u>, and the next lot of interest is calculated using the <u>new total</u> rather than the original amount.

 Daniel invests £10 000 in a savings account which pays 4% compound interest per annum. How much money will there be in his account after 3 years?

1) Work out the <u>multiplier</u>: Multiplier = 4% increase = 1.04

2) Find the amount in the savings account <u>each year</u> until you get to <u>3 years</u>.

After 1 year: £10 000 × 1.04 = £10 400
After 2 years: £10 400 × 1.04 = £10 816
After 3 years: £10 816 × 1.04 = £11 248.64

'Per annum' just means 'each year'.

<u>Compound decay</u> (depreciation) questions are about things that <u>decrease</u> in value or number over time.

EXAMPLE: Susan has just bought a car for £6500. The car depreciates by 8% each year. How many years will it be before the car is worth less than £5000?

1) Work out the <u>multiplier</u>: 8% decrease = 1 − 0.08 = 0.92

2) Calculate the value of the car <u>each year</u> — stop when the value drops <u>below £5000</u>.

After 1 year: £6500 × 0.92 = £5980
After 2 years: £5980 × 0.92 = £5501.60
After 3 years: £5501.60 × 0.92 = £5061.472
After 4 years: £5061.472 × 0.92 = £4656.55424

So it will be **4 years** before the car is worth less than £5000.

The Formula

If you're feeling confident with compound growth and decay then <u>learn this formula</u>. It'll speed things up...

Amount after n days/hours/years $\longrightarrow$ $N = N_0 \times (\text{multiplier})^n$ $\longleftarrow$ Number of days/hours/years

Initial amount   Percentage change multiplier

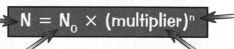

EXAMPLE: The number of bacteria in a sample increases at a rate of 40% each day. Initially, there were 1000 bacteria. How many bacteria will there be after 10 days? Give your answer to the nearest 1000.

1) Work out the <u>multiplier</u>: Multiplier = 40% increase = 1.4

2) Put an <u>initial value</u> of 1000, a <u>time</u> of 10 days and the <u>multiplier</u> into the formula.

$1000 \times 1.4^{10} = 28\,925.465...$

So after 10 days there will be 29 000 bacteria (to the nearest 1000).

I thought you'd depreciate all the work I've put into this page...

Write down the value after each increase/decrease — it'll help you keep track of where you're up to.

Q1 Pippa's bank account pays 2.5% compound interest per annum and her bank balance is £3200. After 3 years, how much will Pippa's bank balance be? [3 marks]

Unit Conversions

A nice easy page for a change — just some <u>facts</u> to learn. Hooray!

Metric and Imperial Units

COMMON METRIC CONVERSIONS	
1 cm = 10 mm	1 tonne = 1000 kg
1 m = 100 cm	1 litre = 1000 ml
1 km = 1000 m	1 litre = 1000 cm³
1 kg = 1000 g	1 cm³ = 1 ml

COMMON IMPERIAL CONVERSIONS	
1 Yard = 3 Feet	1 Foot = 12 Inches
1 Gallon = 8 Pints	
1 Stone = 14 Pounds	
1 Pound = 16 Ounces	

You only need to <u>remember</u> the <u>metric</u> conversions, but you should be able to <u>use</u> them <u>all</u>.

COMMON METRIC-IMPERIAL CONVERSIONS			
1 kg ≈ 2.2 pounds	1 foot ≈ 30 cm	1 gallon ≈ 4.5 litres	1 mile ≈ 1.6 km

≈ means approximately equal to

3 Step Method for Converting Units

① Find the <u>conversion factor</u> (always easy).

② <u>Multiply AND divide by it</u>.

③ Choose the <u>common sense answer</u>.

Make sure you cross out the incorrect working or you could lose marks.

---

1 Convert 7 litres into ml.

1) Find the <u>conversion factor</u>.

2) <u>Multiply</u> and <u>divide</u> by it.

3) Choose the <u>sensible</u> answer — there should be <u>more millilitres than litres</u>.

1 litre = 1000 ml, so conversion factor = 1000

7 × 1000 = 7000   ~~7 ÷ 1000 = 0.007~~

7 litres = 7000 ml

2 Neil's jetski can hold 116 pints of fuel. How many gallons is this? (1 gallon = 8 pints)

1) Find the <u>conversion factor</u>.

2) <u>Multiply</u> and <u>divide</u> by it.

3) Choose the <u>sensible</u> answer — there should be <u>fewer gallons than pints</u>.

1 gallon = 8 pints, so conversion factor = 8

~~116 × 8 = 928~~   116 ÷ 8 = 14.5

116 pints = 14.5 gallons

---

3 Igor unicycles 8 miles to work. How far is this in km? (1 mile ≈ 1.6 km)

1) Find the <u>conversion factor</u>.

2) <u>Multiply</u> and <u>divide</u> by it.

3) Choose the <u>sensible</u> answer — there should be <u>more km than miles</u>.

1 mile ≈ 1.6 km, so conversion factor = 1.6

8 × 1.6 = 12.8   ~~8 ÷ 1.6 = 5~~

8 miles ≈ 12.8 km

Learn how to convert these questions into marks...

Hmm, I don't know about you, but I quite fancy a conversion-based question after all that.

Q1 A squash court is 9.75 m long. 1 foot ≈ 30 cm and 1 foot = 12 inches.

 a) How long is the court in cm? [1 mark]   b) How long is the court in feet and inches? [2 marks]

Area and Volume Conversions

Time for some <u>trickier conversions</u> to sink your teeth into. There are a <u>couple of methods</u> for you to remember so that when it comes to the exam you can feel confident converting areas and volumes.

Converting Areas

You need to be really <u>careful</u> when converting areas — just because 1 m = 100 cm <u>DOES NOT</u> mean 1 m² = 100 cm².

Follow this <u>method</u> to avoid slipping up:

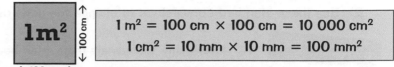

1m²

$1 m^2 = 100 cm \times 100 cm = 10\ 000 cm^2$
$1 cm^2 = 10 mm \times 10 mm = 100 mm^2$

← 100 cm →

1) Find the <u>conversion factor</u> — it'll be the same as for converting units (see p66).
2) <u>Multiply AND divide</u> by the conversion factor <u>TWO TIMES</u>.
3) Choose the <u>common sense answer</u>, and don't forget that the units come with a <u>2</u>, e.g. mm², cm².

EXAMPLE: The area of the top of a table is 0.6 m². Find its area in cm².

1) Find the <u>conversion factor</u>:   1 m = 100 cm ⟶ Conversion factor = 100

2) It's an area — multiply and divide <u>twice</u> by the conversion factor: $0.6 \times 100 \times 100 = 6000$
$0.6 \div 100 \div 100 = 0.00006$ ~~0.6 ÷ 100 ÷ 100 = 0.00006~~

1 m = 100 cm so expect <u>more</u> cm than m.

3) Choose the <u>sensible</u> answer: 0.6 m² = 6000 cm²

Converting Volumes

$1 m^3 = 100 cm \times 100 cm \times 100 cm = 1\ 000\ 000 cm^3$
$1 cm^3 = 10 mm \times 10 mm \times 10 mm = 1000 mm^3$

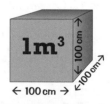

1m³

← 100 cm →

1) Find the <u>conversion factor</u> — it'll be the same as for converting units (see p66).
2) <u>Multiply AND divide</u> by the conversion factor <u>THREE TIMES</u>.
3) Choose the <u>common sense answer</u>, and don't forget that the units come with a <u>3</u>, e.g. mm³, cm³.

EXAMPLE: A glass has a volume of 72 000 mm³. What is its volume in cm³?

1) Find the <u>conversion factor</u>:   1 cm = 10 mm ⟶ Conversion factor = 10

2) It's a volume — multiply and divide <u>3 times</u> by the conversion factor: ~~72 000 × 10 × 10 × 10 = 72 000 000~~
$72\ 000 \div 10 \div 10 \div 10 = 72$

1 cm = 10 mm, so expect <u>fewer</u> cm than mm.

3) Choose the <u>sensible</u> answer: 72 000 mm³ = 72 cm³

That's it, you've converted me, I love maths...

For areas use the conversion factor twice, for volumes use it three times. Have a go at these questions:

Q1   The area of a forest is 6 km². What is its area in m²?   [2 marks]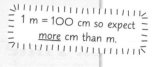

Q2   The volume of a golf ball is 40 cm³. What is its volume in mm³?   [2 marks]

Time Intervals

Make sure you can convert between <u>time units</u> — it's <u>simple</u> and might grab you a mark or two in the exam.

Converting Time Units

| 1 day = 24 hours |
| 1 hour = 60 minutes |
| 1 minute = 60 seconds |

1) You ought to know the standard <u>time unit conversions</u> by now.
2) Use these standard conversions to change the units of <u>other times</u>.

EXAMPLES:

1. How many seconds are there in an hour?

1) First convert <u>hours</u> into <u>minutes</u>.   1 hour = 60 minutes
2) Then convert <u>minutes</u> into <u>seconds</u>.   60 minutes = 60 × 60 = 3600 seconds

---

Be <u>very careful</u> when using <u>calculators</u> — the decimal answers they give are confusing, e.g. <u>2.5 hours = 2 hours 30 mins</u>, <u>NOT 2 hours 50 mins</u>.

2. Write 186 minutes in hours and minutes.

1) Work out how many <u>complete hours</u> there are in 186 minutes.

   2 hours = 2 × 60 = 120 minutes
   3 hours = 3 × 60 = 180 minutes ✓
   4 hours = 4 × 60 = 240 minutes — too many

2) Find how many <u>minutes over 3 hours</u> it is.

   186 − 180 = <u>6 minutes</u>
   So 186 minutes = 3 hours 6 minutes

Break Time Calculations into Simple Stages

EXAMPLE: Angela watched a film that started at 7.20 pm and finished at 10.05 pm. How long was the film in minutes?

1) Split the time between 7.20 pm and 10.05 pm into <u>simple stages</u>.

   7.20 pm   9.20 pm   10.00 pm   10.05 pm
     + 2 hours   + 40 minutes   + 5 minutes

2) <u>Convert</u> the hours to minutes.   2 hours = 2 × 60 = 120 minutes

3) <u>Add</u> to get the total minutes.   120 + 40 + 5 = **165 minutes**

Timetables

EXAMPLE: Use the timetable to answer this question.

Harry wants to get a bus from the <u>bus station</u> to the <u>train station</u> in time for a train that leaves at <u>19:30</u>. What is the latest bus he can catch?

Bus Timetable				
Bus Station	18 45	19 00	19 15	19 30
Market Street	18 52	19 07	19 22	19 37
Long Lane	19 01	19 16	19 31	19 46
Train Station	19 11	19 26	19 41	19 56

1) Read along the <u>train station</u> row.   19 11   (19 26)   19 41   19 56

This is the latest time he could arrive before 19:30.

2) Move up this column to the <u>bus station</u> row and read off the entry.

The bus that gets to the train station at 19:26 leaves the bus station at **19:00**.

Got a friend who's always late? Show them this page...

Calculators really are a nightmare when it comes to working with time intervals. Try these questions:

Q1   a) How many minutes are there in 2 days?   [1 mark]
      b) Write 265 seconds in minutes and seconds.   [2 marks]

Q2   Zoe works 4 days a week at an owl sanctuary. She starts work at 6.20 am and finishes at 12.50 pm. She earns £7.20 per hour. How much does she earn in a week?   [3 marks]

Speed, Density and Pressure

Let's see if you can speed through this page. You need to know the <u>formulas</u> and be able to bung numbers into them — you should also be able to <u>convert</u> between different <u>units</u> (which is a bit tricky).

Speed = Distance ÷ Time

Speed is the <u>distance travelled per unit time</u> — the number of <u>km per hour</u> or <u>metres per second</u>.

$$\text{SPEED} = \frac{\text{DISTANCE}}{\text{TIME}} \qquad \text{TIME} = \frac{\text{DISTANCE}}{\text{SPEED}} \qquad \text{DISTANCE} = \text{SPEED} \times \text{TIME}$$

A <u>formula triangle</u> is a mighty handy tool for remembering formulas. Here's the one for speed.
To <u>remember the order of the letters</u> (S^{D}T) we have the words <u>SaD Times</u>.
So if it's a question on speed, distance and time, just say <u>SAD TIMES</u>.

HOW DO YOU USE FORMULA TRIANGLES?
1) <u>COVER UP</u> the thing you want to find and <u>WRITE DOWN</u> what's left.
2) Now <u>PUT IN THE VALUES</u> for the other two things and <u>WORK IT OUT</u>.

E.g. to get the formula for <u>speed</u> from the triangle, cover up <u>S</u> and you're left with $\frac{D}{T}$.

EXAMPLES:

1. Rob cycles 18 miles in 2 hours. What is his average speed?

1) You want speed so <u>covering S</u> gives: $S = \frac{D}{T}$
2) <u>Put in</u> the numbers — and don't forget the units. $S = 18 \div 2 = 9$ mph

CHECK YOUR UNITS MATCH
If the distance is in <u>miles</u> and the time is in <u>hours</u> then you'll get a speed in <u>mph</u>.

2. A cheetah runs at a constant speed of 27 m/s for 20 s. What distance does it cover?

1) You want distance so <u>covering D</u> gives: $D = S \times T$
2) <u>Put in</u> the numbers — and don't forget the units. $D = 27 \times 20 = 540$ m

UNITS CHECK: m/s and s go in so m comes out.

Density = Mass ÷ Volume

Density is the <u>mass per unit volume</u> of a substance. It's usually measured in <u>kg/m³</u> or <u>g/cm³</u>.

$$\text{DENSITY} = \frac{\text{MASS}}{\text{VOLUME}} \qquad \text{VOLUME} = \frac{\text{MASS}}{\text{DENSITY}} \qquad \text{MASS} = \text{DENSITY} \times \text{VOLUME}$$

Here's the formula triangle for <u>density</u>. To remember the order of the letters in the formula triangle think D^{M}V or <u>DiMoV</u> (the Russian agent).

EXAMPLE: A giant 'Wunda-Choc' bar has a density of 1.3 g/cm³. If the bar's volume is 1800 cm³, what is the mass of the bar in grams?

1) You want the mass, so <u>covering M</u> gives: $M = D \times V$
2) Put in the <u>numbers</u> — and remember the <u>units</u>. $M = 1.3 \text{ g/cm}^3 \times 1800 \text{ cm}^3 = 2340$ g

UNITS CHECK: g/cm³ and cm³ go in so g comes out.

Speed, Density and Pressure

Pressure = Force ÷ Area

'N' stands for 'Newtons'.

Pressure is the amount of <u>force acting per unit area</u>. It's usually measured in <u>N/m²</u>, or pascals (Pa).

PRESSURE = $\frac{FORCE}{AREA}$	AREA = $\frac{FORCE}{PRESSURE}$	FORCE = PRESSURE × AREA

Another formula triangle here — this one's for <u>pressure</u>. When you come across a pressure question, a handy trick to <u>remember the order</u> of the letters (P^{F}A) is to put on your best Spanish accent and say "<u>ohhh PerFectA</u>".

EXAMPLE: A cuboid box with a weight of 200 N rests on horizontal ground. The side lengths of the face resting on the ground are 0.2 m and 0.8 m. Calculate the pressure exerted by the box on the ground.

1) Work out the <u>area of the face</u> in contact with the ground: 0.2 m × 0.8 m = 0.16 m²

2) Use the <u>formula triangle</u> — you want pressure so <u>covering P</u> gives: $P = \frac{F}{A}$

3) Put in the <u>numbers</u>. $P = \frac{200\,N}{0.16\,m^2}$

4) <u>Check the units</u> — you put in <u>N</u> and <u>m²</u> so you'll get <u>N/m²</u>.   = 1250 N/m²

Converting Speed, Density and Pressure (5)

1) Units of speed, density and pressure are made up of <u>two measures</u> — a <u>distance</u> and a <u>time</u>, a <u>mass</u> and a <u>volume</u>, or a <u>force</u> and an <u>area</u>.

2) So to <u>convert units</u> of speed, density or pressure, you might need to do <u>two conversions</u> — one for each measure.

EXAMPLE: A rabbit's top speed is 54 km/h. How fast is this in m/s?

1) First convert from km/h to m/h: 1 km = 1000 m, so conversion factor = 1000
54 × 1000 = 54 000   ~~54 ÷ 1000 = 0.054~~
54 km/h = 54 000 m/h

2) Now convert from m/h to m/s: 1 hour = 60 minutes = 60 × 60 = 3600 seconds
So conversion factor = 3600
~~54 000 × 3600 = 194 400 000~~   54 000 ÷ 3600 = 15
54 km/h = 54 000 m/h = 15 m/s

Formula triangles — it's all a big cover-up...

Write down the formula triangles from the last two pages, then use them to generate all nine formulas.

Q1   A cylinder rests with its 8 m² circular face on horizontal ground. The pressure it exerts on the ground is 350 N/m². What is the force of the cylinder on the ground?   [2 marks] (4)

Q2   A sprinter runs 400 m in 50 seconds.   a) What was his average speed in m/s?   [1 mark]
   b) What was his average speed in km/h?   [3 marks] (5)

Q3   A cube has a mass of 25 g and side length 2 cm.
a) What is the density in g/cm³? [2 marks]   b) What is the density in kg/m³?   [3 marks] (5)

Revision Questions for Section Four

Lots of things to remember in <u>Section Four</u> — there's only one way to find out what you've taken in...
- Try these questions and <u>tick off each one</u> when you <u>get it right</u>.
- When you've done <u>all the questions</u> for a topic and are <u>completely happy</u> with it, tick off the topic.

Ratios (p55-57) ☑

1) Reduce: a) 18:22 to its simplest form   b) 49 g:14 g to the form n:1 ☑

2) Sarah is in charge of ordering stock for a clothes shop. The shop usually sells red scarves and blue scarves in the ratio 5:8. Sarah orders 50 red scarves. How many blue scarves should she order? ☑

3) Pencils and rubbers are in the ratio 7:2. How many times more pencils are there than rubbers? ☑

4) Ryan, Joel and Sam are sharing 800 lollipops. They split the lollipops in the ratio 5:8:12.
   a) What fraction of the lollipops does Ryan get?   b) How many lollipops does Sam get? ☑

Proportion Problems (p58-60) ☑

5) The recipe on the right shows CGP's secret pasta sauce recipe. The recipe serves 6 people. How much of each ingredient is needed to make enough for 17 servings?

   - 18 ml olive oil
   - 360 g tomatoes
   - 9 g garlic powder
   - 72 g onions ☑

6) 3 gardeners can plant 360 flowers in a day. How many flowers could 8 gardeners plant in a day? ☑

7) 'y is directly proportional to x'. Sketch the graph of this proportion for $x \geq 0$. ☑

8) A DIY shop sells varnish in two different sized tins. A 500 ml tin costs £8 and a 1800 ml tin costs £30. Which tin represents the best value for money? ☑

9) The amount of time it takes to wash a car is inversely proportional to the number of people washing it. 3 people take 12 minutes to wash a car. How many people are needed to wash a car in 2 minutes? ☑

Percentages (p61-65) ☐

10) If x = 20 and y = 95:   a) Find x% of y.   b) Find the new value after y is increased by x%.
                             c) Express x as a percentage of y.   d) Express y as a percentage of x. ☑

11) What's the formula for finding a change in value as a percentage? ☑

12) An antique wardrobe decreased in value from £800 to £520. What was the percentage decrease? ☑

13) A tree's height has increased by 15% in the last year to 20.24 m. What was its height a year ago? ☑

14) 25% of the items sold by a bakery in one day were pies. 8% of the pies sold were chicken pies. What percentage of the items sold by the bakery were chicken pies? ☑

15) Collectable baseball cards increase in value by 10% each year. A particular card is worth £80.
    a) How much will it be worth in 4 years?   b) In how many years will it be worth over £140? ☑

Conversions and Time (p66-68) ☑

16) Convert: a) 5.6 litres to cm^3 b) 8 feet to cm   c) 2 weeks into hours
              d) 12 m^3 to cm^3 e) 1280 mm^2 to cm^2 f) 2.75 cm^3 to mm^3 ☑

17) A musical production starts at 19:30. The musical is 118 minutes long plus a 20 minute interval. What time does the musical finish? Give your answer in 12-hour time. ☑

Speed, Density and Pressure (p69-70) ☑

18) Find the average speed, in km/h, of a car if it travels 63 miles in 1.5 hours. ☑

19) Find the volume, in cm^3, of a snowman if its density is 0.4 g/cm^3 and its mass is 5000 g. ☑

20) Find the area of an object in contact with horizontal ground, if the pressure it exerts on the ground is 120 N/m^2 and the force acting on the object is 1320 N. ☑

Properties of 2D Shapes

Here's a nice easy page to get you started on 2D shapes.

Line Symmetry

This is where you draw one or more **MIRROR LINES** across a shape and both sides will fold exactly together.

| 2 LINES OF SYMMETRY | 1 LINE OF SYMMETRY | 1 LINE OF SYMMETRY | 3 LINES OF SYMMETRY | NO LINES OF SYMMETRY | 1 LINE OF SYMMETRY |

Rotational Symmetry

This is where you can rotate the shape into different positions that look exactly the same.

| Order 1 | Order 2 | Order 2 | Order 3 | Order 4 |

The **ORDER OF ROTATIONAL SYMMETRY** is the posh way of saying: 'how many different positions look the same'. You should say the Z-shape above has 'rotational symmetry of order 2'.

When a shape has only 1 position you can either say that it has 'rotational symmetry of order 1' or that it has 'NO rotational symmetry'.

Regular Polygons

All the sides and angles in a regular polygon are the same.
Learn the names of these regular polygons and how many sides they have.
(An equilateral triangle and a square are both regular polygons — see the next page for their properties.)

In an irregular polygon, the sides and angles aren't all equal.

 REGULAR PENTAGON
5 sides
5 lines of symmetry
Rotational symmetry of order 5

 REGULAR HEXAGON
6 sides
6 lines of symmetry
Rotational symmetry of order 6

 REGULAR HEPTAGON
7 sides
7 lines of symmetry
Rotational symmetry of order 7

 REGULAR OCTAGON
8 sides
8 lines of symmetry
Rotational symmetry of order 8

 REGULAR NONAGON
9 sides
9 lines of symmetry
Rotational symmetry of order 9

 REGULAR DECAGON
10 sides
10 lines of symmetry
Rotational symmetry of order 10

Mirror line, mirror line on the wall...

Make sure you learn the two different types of symmetry, and dazzle your friends by spotting them in everyday shapes like road signs, warning signs and letters.

Q1   Make two copies of the pattern to the right.
   a) Shade two squares to make a pattern with one line of symmetry.   [2 marks]
   b) Shade two squares to make a pattern with rotational symmetry of order 2.   [2 marks]

Properties of 2D Shapes

This page is jam-packed with details about <u>triangles</u> and <u>quadrilaterals</u> — and you need to learn them all.

Triangles

1) **EQUILATERAL TRIANGLES**

   <u>3 equal sides</u> and
   <u>3 equal angles</u> of <u>60°</u>.
   <u>3 lines</u> of symmetry,
   rotational symmetry <u>order 3</u>.

2) **RIGHT-ANGLED TRIANGLES**

   1 <u>right angle</u> (90°).
   <u>No</u> lines of symmetry.
   <u>No</u> rotational symmetry.

The little square means it's a right angle.

3) **ISOSCELES TRIANGLES**

   <u>2 sides</u> the same.
   <u>2 angles</u> the same.
   <u>1 line</u> of symmetry.
   <u>No</u> rotational symmetry.

These dashes mean that the two sides are the same length.

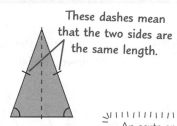

4) **SCALENE TRIANGLES**

   All three sides <u>different</u>.
   All three angles <u>different</u>.
   No symmetry (pretty obviously).

An <u>acute-angled triangle</u> has 3 acute angles, and an <u>obtuse-angled triangle</u> has one obtuse angle (see p87).

Quadrilaterals

1) **SQUARE**

 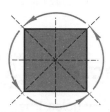

   <u>4 equal angles</u> of <u>90°</u> (right angles).
   <u>4 lines</u> of symmetry, rotational symmetry <u>order 4</u>.

2) **RECTANGLE**

 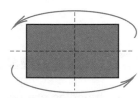

   <u>4 equal angles</u> of <u>90°</u> (right angles).
   <u>2 lines</u> of symmetry, rotational symmetry <u>order 2</u>.

3) **RHOMBUS** (A square pushed over)

Matching arrows show parallel sides.

A rhombus is the same as a <u>diamond</u>.

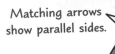 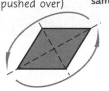 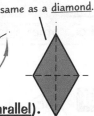

   <u>4 equal sides</u> (opposite sides are <u>parallel</u>).
   <u>2 pairs</u> of <u>equal angles</u>.
   <u>2 lines</u> of symmetry, rotational symmetry <u>order 2</u>.

4) **PARALLELOGRAM** (A rectangle pushed over)

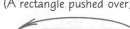 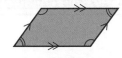 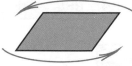

   <u>2 pairs</u> of <u>equal sides</u> (each pair are <u>parallel</u>).
   <u>2 pairs</u> of <u>equal angles</u>.
   <u>NO lines</u> of symmetry, rotational symmetry <u>order 2</u>.

5) **TRAPEZIUM**

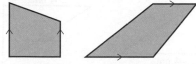

   <u>1 pair</u> of <u>parallel sides</u>.
   <u>NO lines</u> of symmetry*.
   No rotational symmetry.

*In an isosceles trapezium, the sloping sides are the same length. An isosceles trapezium has 1 line of symmetry.

6) **KITE**

   <u>2 pairs</u> of <u>equal sides</u>.
   <u>1 pair</u> of <u>equal angles</u>.
   <u>1 line</u> of symmetry.
   No rotational symmetry.

Kite facts — 2 pairs of equal sides, 1 line of symmetry, Gemini...

Learn the <u>names</u> (and spellings) and <u>properties</u> of all the shapes on this page, then try this question:

Q1 A quadrilateral has all 4 sides the same length and two pairs of equal angles.
Identify the quadrilateral, and write down its order of rotational symmetry. [2 marks]

Congruent Shapes

Shapes can be <u>congruent</u>. And I bet you really want to know what that means — I can already picture your eager face. Well, lucky you — I've written a page all about it.

Congruent — Same Shape, Same Size

<u>Congruence</u> is another ridiculous maths word which sounds really complicated when it's not:

> If two shapes are <u>CONGRUENT</u>, they are <u>EXACTLY THE SAME</u>
> — the <u>SAME SIZE</u> and the <u>SAME SHAPE</u>.

There ain't room for the two of us in this town, pal.

These shapes are all <u>congruent</u>:

A B

C D

Note — you can have <u>mirror images</u> or <u>rotations</u>.

EXAMPLE: Two of the triangles below are congruent. Write down the letters of the congruent triangles.

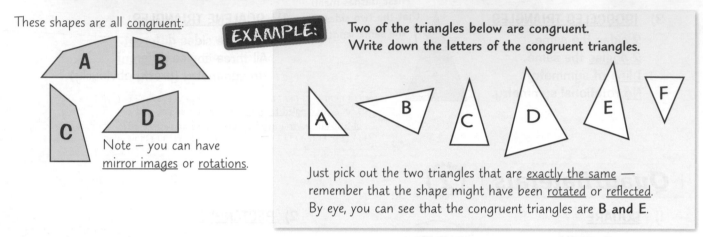

Just pick out the two triangles that are <u>exactly the same</u> — remember that the shape might have been <u>rotated</u> or <u>reflected</u>. By eye, you can see that the congruent triangles are **B and E**.

Conditions for Congruent Triangles

<u>Two triangles</u> are <u>congruent</u> if <u>one</u> of the four conditions below holds true:

1) <u>SSS</u>   <u>three sides</u> are the same
2) <u>AAS</u>   <u>two angles</u> and a <u>corresponding side</u> match up
3) <u>SAS</u>   <u>two sides</u> and the <u>angle between them</u> match up
4) <u>RHS</u>   a <u>right angle</u>, the <u>hypotenuse</u> and one other <u>side</u> all match up

The <u>hypotenuse</u> is the <u>longest side</u> of a right-angled triangle — the one <u>opposite</u> the <u>right angle</u>.

Make sure the sides match up — here, the side is opposite the 81° angle.

SAS? More like SOS...

Once you've memorised the four conditions above, have a go at this question.

Q1   The two triangles shown on the right are congruent.
Find the values of x, y and z.   [2 marks]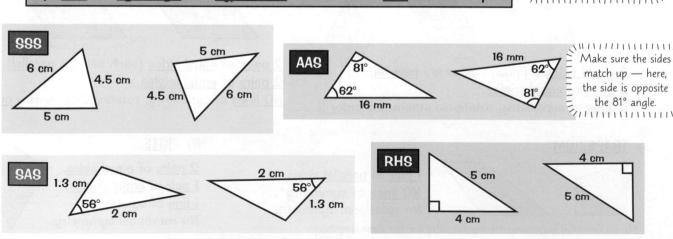

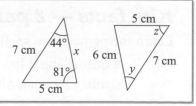

Similar Shapes

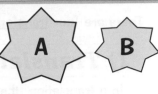

Similar shapes are <u>exactly the same shape</u>, but can be <u>different sizes</u> (they can also be <u>rotated</u> or <u>reflected</u>).

<u>SIMILAR</u> — same shape, <u>different size</u>.

Similar Shapes Have the Same Angles

GRADE 5

Generally, for two shapes to be <u>similar</u>, all the <u>angles</u> must match and the <u>sides</u> must be <u>proportional</u>. But for <u>triangles</u>, there are <u>three special conditions</u> — if any one of these is true, you know they're similar.

Two triangles are similar if:

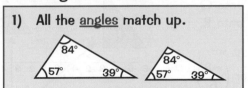

1) All the <u>angles</u> match up.

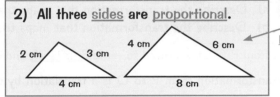

2) All three <u>sides</u> are <u>proportional</u>.

Here, the sides of the <u>bigger</u> triangle are <u>twice</u> as long as the sides of the <u>smaller</u> triangle.

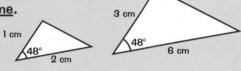

3) Any <u>two sides</u> are <u>proportional</u> and the <u>angle between them</u> is the <u>same</u>.

Watch out — if one of the triangles has been rotated or flipped over, it might look as if they're not similar, but don't be fooled.

EXAMPLE: Tony says, "Triangles ABC and DEF are similar." Is Tony correct? Explain your answer.

<u>Check</u> condition 3 holds — start by finding the <u>missing angle</u> in triangle DEF:

Angle DEF = 180° − 46° − 30° = 104° so angle ABC = angle DEF

Now check that <u>AB</u> and <u>BC</u> are <u>proportional</u> to <u>DE</u> and <u>EF</u>:

DE ÷ AB = 6 ÷ 2 = 3 and EF ÷ BC = 9 ÷ 3 = 3 so DE and EF are 3 times as long as AB and BC.

Tony is correct — two sides are proportional and the angle between them is the same so the triangles are similar.

Use Similarity to Find Missing Lengths

GRADE 5

You might have to use the <u>properties</u> of similar shapes to find missing distances, lengths etc. — you'll need to use <u>scale factors</u> (see p.77) to find the lengths of missing sides.

EXAMPLE: ABC and ADE are similar right-angled triangles. AC = 20 cm, AE = 50 cm and BC = 8 cm. Find the length of DE.

The triangles are <u>similar</u>, so work out the <u>scale factor</u>:

scale factor = $\frac{50}{20}$ = <u>2.5</u>

Now <u>use</u> the scale factor to work out the length of DE:

DE = 8 × 2.5 = <u>20 cm</u>

Butter and margarine — similar products...

To help remember the difference between similarity and congruence, think '<u>similar siblings, congruent clones</u>' — siblings are alike but not the same, clones are identical.

Q1   Find the length of BD.   [3 marks] **GRADE 5**

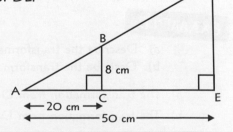

The Four Transformations

There are four <u>transformations</u> you need to know — <u>translation</u>, <u>rotation</u>, <u>reflection</u> and <u>enlargement</u>.

1) Translations

In a <u>translation</u>, the <u>amount</u> the shape moves by is given as a <u>vector</u> (see p.103-104) written $\binom{x}{y}$ — where x is the <u>horizontal movement</u> (i.e. to the <u>right</u>) and y is the <u>vertical movement</u> (i.e. <u>up</u>). If the shape moves <u>left and down</u>, x and y will be <u>negative</u>.

EXAMPLE:
a) Describe the transformation that maps triangle P onto Q.
b) Describe the transformation that maps triangle P onto R.

a) To get from P to Q, you need to move <u>8 units left</u> and <u>6 units up</u>, so...

The transformation from P to Q is a **translation by the vector** $\binom{-8}{6}$.

b) The transformation from P to R is a **translation by the vector** $\binom{0}{7}$.

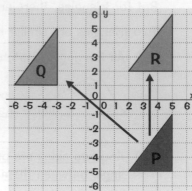

2) Rotations

To describe a <u>rotation</u>, you must give <u>3 details</u>:
1) The <u>angle of rotation</u> (usually 90° or 180°).
2) The <u>direction of rotation</u> (clockwise or anticlockwise).
3) The <u>centre of rotation</u> (often, but not always, the origin).

For a rotation of 180°, it doesn't matter whether you go clockwise or anticlockwise.

EXAMPLE:
a) Describe the transformation that maps triangle A onto B.
b) Describe the transformation that maps triangle A onto C.

a) The transformation from A to B is a **rotation of 90° anticlockwise** about the **origin**.

b) The transformation from A to C is a **rotation of 180° clockwise** (or anticlockwise) about the **origin**.

If it helps, you can use tracing paper to help you find the centre of rotation.

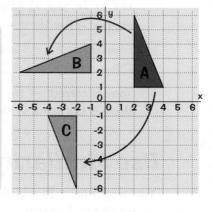

3) Reflections

For a <u>reflection</u>, you must give the <u>equation</u> of the <u>mirror line</u>.

EXAMPLE:
a) Describe the transformation that maps shape D onto shape E.
b) Describe the transformation that maps shape D onto shape F.

a) The transformation from D to E is a **reflection in the y-axis**.

b) The transformation from D to F is a **reflection in the line $y = x$**.

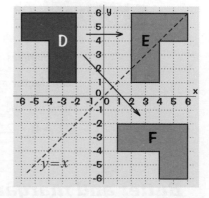

Moving eet to ze left — a perfect translation...

Shapes are <u>congruent</u> under translation, reflection and rotation — this is because their <u>size</u> and <u>shape</u> don't change, just their position and orientation. Now have a go at this question:

Q1   On a grid, copy shape D above and rotate it 90° clockwise about the point (−1, −1).   [2 marks]

The Four Transformations

One more transformation coming up — <u>enlargements</u>. They're the trickiest, but also the most fun (honest).

4) Enlargements

For an <u>enlargement</u>, you must specify:

> 1) The <u>scale factor</u>.
> 2) The <u>centre of enlargement</u>.

$$\text{scale factor} = \frac{\text{new length}}{\text{old length}}$$

1) The <u>scale factor</u> for an enlargement tells you <u>how long</u> the sides of the new shape are compared to the old shape. E.g. a scale factor of 3 means you <u>multiply</u> each side length by 3.

2) If you're given the <u>centre of enlargement</u>, then it's vitally important <u>where</u> your new shape is on the grid.

> The <u>scale factor</u> tells you the <u>RELATIVE DISTANCE</u> of the old points and new points from the <u>centre of enlargement</u>.

So, a <u>scale factor of 2</u> means the corners of the enlarged shape are <u>twice as far from the centre of enlargement</u> as the corners of the original shape.

Describing Enlargements

EXAMPLE: Describe the transformation that maps Triangle A onto Triangle B.

Use the formula to find the <u>scale factor</u>. (Just do this for one pair of sides.)

Old length of triangle base = 3 units
New length of triangle base = 6 units

Scale factor $= \dfrac{\text{new length}}{\text{old length}} = \dfrac{6}{3} = 2$

To find the <u>centre of enlargement</u>, draw <u>lines</u> that go through <u>matching corners</u> of both shapes and see where they <u>cross</u>.

So the transformation is an enlargement of scale factor 2, centre (2, 6).

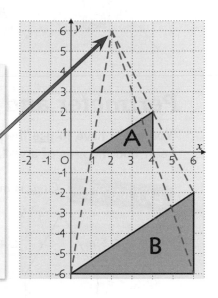

Fractional Scale Factors

1) If the scale factor is <u>bigger than 1</u> the <u>shape gets bigger</u>.
2) If the scale factor is <u>smaller than 1</u> (e.g. ½) it <u>gets smaller</u>.

EXAMPLE: Enlarge the shaded shape by a <u>scale factor of</u> $\frac{1}{2}$, about <u>centre O</u>.

1) <u>Draw lines</u> going from the <u>centre</u> to <u>each corner</u> of the original shape. The corners of the new shape will be on these lines.

2) The scale factor is $\frac{1}{2}$, so make <u>each corner</u> of the new shape <u>half as far</u> from O as it is in the original shape.

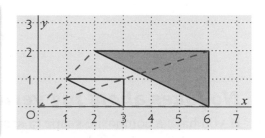

Scale factors — they're enough to put the fear of cod into you...

Shapes are similar under enlargement — the position and the size change, but the angles and ratios of the sides don't (see p.75).

Q1 On a grid, draw triangle A with vertices (2, 1), (4, 1) and (4, 3), and triangle B with vertices (3, 1), (7, 1) and (7, 5). Describe the transformation that maps A to B. [4 marks]

Perimeter and Area

Perimeter is the distance around the outside of a shape. Area is a bit trickier — you need to learn some formulas.
You should already know that the area of a rectangle is $A = l \times w$ and the area of a square is $A = l^2$.

Area Formulas for Triangles and Quadrilaterals

Learn these formulas:

Area of triangle = ½ × base × vertical height

$$A = \tfrac{1}{2} \times b \times h$$

Note that in each case the height must be the vertical height, not the sloping height.

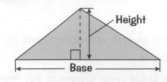

$$\text{Area of parallelogram} = \text{base} \times \text{vertical height}$$

$$A = b \times h$$

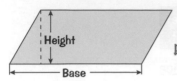

Area of trapezium = average of parallel sides × distance between them (vertical height)

$$A = \tfrac{1}{2}(a + b) \times h$$

Perimeter and Area Problems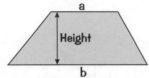

You might have to use the perimeter or area of a shape to answer a slightly more complicated question
(e.g. find the area of a wall, then work out how many rolls of wallpaper you need to wallpaper it).

EXAMPLE: Greg is making a stained-glass window in the shape shown below.

When you're adding side lengths it's a good idea to mark them off as you go along to make sure you don't repeat or miss any.

a) **Find the perimeter of the window.**
Label all the side lengths, then add them up:
0.5 m + 1.2 m + 0.6 m + 1.2 m + 0.5 m = 4 m

b) **Coloured glass costs £82 per m². Work out the cost of the glass needed for the window.**
Split the shape into a triangle and a rectangle (as shown) to find the area:
Area of rectangle = length × width = 0.6 × 1.2 = 0.72 m²
Area of triangle = $\frac{1}{2}$ × base × height = $\frac{1}{2}$ × 0.6 × 0.4 = 0.12 m²
Total area of shape = 0.72 + 0.12 = 0.84 m²

Then multiply the area by the price to work out the cost:
Cost = area × price per m² = 0.84 × 82 = £68.88

No jokes about my vertical height please...

If you have a composite shape (a shape made up of different shapes stuck together), split it into triangles
and quadrilaterals, work out the area of each bit and add them together.

Q1   A shape is made up of a triangle and a parallelogram. The triangle has base length 3 cm
and the parallelogram has base length 11 cm. They both have a vertical height of 6 cm.
Find the total area of the shape.   [3 marks]

Q2   The triangle and rectangle shown on the right have
the same area. Find the value of x.   [2 marks]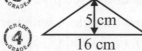

Perimeter and Area — Circles

Yes, I thought I could detect some groaning when you realised that this is another page of formulas. You know the drill...

LEARN these Formulas

Area and Circumference of Circles

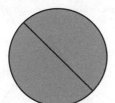

__Area of circle__ = π × (radius)²
Remember that the radius is half the diameter.

$$A = \pi r^2$$

__Circumference__ = π × diameter
= 2 × π × radius

$$C = \pi D = 2\pi r$$

For these formulas, use the π button on your calculator. For non-calculator questions, use π ≈ 3.142.

Arc Lengths and Areas of Sectors

These next ones are a bit more tricky — before you try and learn the formulas, make sure you know what a sector and an arc are (I've helpfully labelled the diagram below — I'm nice like that).

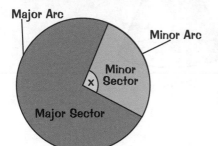
Major Arc / Minor Arc / Minor Sector / x / Major Sector

$$\text{Area of Sector} = \frac{x}{360} \times \text{Area of full Circle}$$

$$\text{Length of Arc} = \frac{x}{360} \times \text{Circumference of full Circle}$$

You also need to know what a segment, a chord and a tangent are.

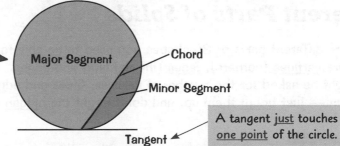
Major Segment / Chord / Minor Segment / Tangent

A tangent __just__ touches __one point__ of the circle.

EXAMPLE: In the diagram on the right, a sector with angle 60° has been cut out of a circle with radius 3 cm. Find the exact area of the shaded shape.

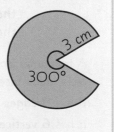
3 cm / 300°

Use the formula to find the area of the shaded sector:

area of sector $= \frac{x}{360} \times \pi r^2 = \frac{300}{360} \times \pi \times 3^2$

$= \frac{5}{6} \times \pi \times 9 = \frac{15}{2} \pi$ cm²

'Exact area' means leave your answer in terms of π.

Pi r not square — pi are round. Pi are tasty...

Oo, one more thing — if you're asked to find the perimeter of a semicircle or quarter circle, don't forget to add on the straight edges too. It's an easy mistake to make, and it'll cost you marks.

Q1 a) For sector A, find:
    (i) the area. Give your answer in terms of π. [2 marks]
    (ii) the arc length, to 2 d.p. [2 marks]
  b) Show that area of sector A is the same as the area of sector B. [2 marks]

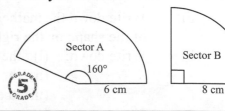
Sector A / 160° / 6 cm / Sector B / 8 cm

3D Shapes

I was going to make some pop-out <u>3D shapes</u> to put on this page, but I couldn't find the scissors and sticky tape. Sorry. Still, you need to learn it all though — so chin up and learn the page.

Eight Solids to Learn

There's more about prisms on p.82.

<u>3D shapes</u> are <u>solid shapes</u>. These are the ones you need to know:

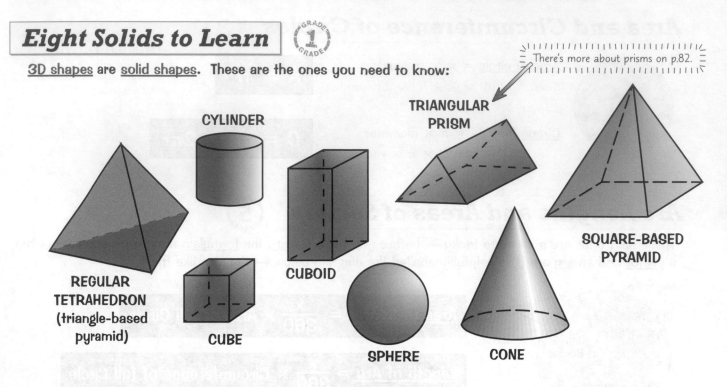

CYLINDER

TRIANGULAR PRISM

SQUARE-BASED PYRAMID

REGULAR TETRAHEDRON (triangle-based pyramid)

CUBOID

CUBE

SPHERE

CONE

Different Parts of Solids

There are different parts of 3D shapes you need to be able to spot. These are <u>vertices</u> (corners), <u>faces</u> (the flat bits) and <u>edges</u>. You might be asked for the <u>number</u> of vertices, faces and edges in the exam — just <u>count</u> them up, and don't forget the <u>hidden</u> ones.

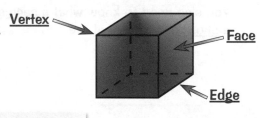

Vertex

Face

Edge

EXAMPLE: For the triangular prism on the right, write down the number of faces, the number of edges and the number of vertices.

Faces (especially curved faces) are sometimes called <u>surfaces</u>.

A triangular prism has **5 faces** (there are three rectangular faces and two triangular ones).

It has **9 edges** (there are 3 hidden ones — the dotted lines in the diagram).

It has **6 vertices** (there's one hidden at the back).

Edge, vertex, face and toes, face and toes. Edge, vertex...

Remember — 1 vertex, 2 vertices. They're funny words, designed to confuse you, so don't let them catch you out. Now have a go at this Exam Practice Question.

Q1 a) Write down the mathematical name
       of the shape on the right.   [1 mark]
    b) Write down: (i) the number of faces   [1 mark]
                    (ii) the number of edges   [1 mark]
                   (iii) the number of vertices   [1 mark]

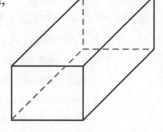

3D Shapes — Surface Area

Surface area is like normal area but for 3D shapes — for some shapes you can use <u>2D areas</u> and add them up, for others there are special <u>formulas</u> you'll need to use.

Surface Area using Nets

1) <u>SURFACE AREA</u> only applies to 3D objects — it's just the <u>total area</u> of all the <u>faces</u> added together.
2) <u>SURFACE AREA OF A SOLID = AREA OF THE NET</u> (remember that a <u>net</u> is just a <u>3D shape</u> folded out flat). So if it helps, imagine (or sketch) the net and add up the area of <u>each bit</u>.

EXAMPLE: Find the surface area of the square-based pyramid below.

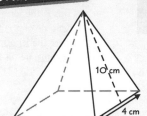

Sketch the net — a square-based pyramid has <u>1 square face</u> and <u>4 triangular faces</u>.

Area of square face = 4 × 4 = 16 cm²
Area of triangular face = ½ × 4 × 10 = 20 cm²
Total surface area = 16 + (4 × 20) = 16 + 80 = 96 cm²

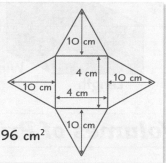

Surface Area Formulas

1) <u>SPHERES, CONES AND CYLINDERS</u> have surface area formulas that you need to be able to use.
2) Luckily you <u>don't</u> need to memorise the <u>sphere</u> and <u>cone</u> formulas — you'll be given them in your exam.
3) But you must get <u>lots of practice</u> using them, or you might slip up when it comes to the exam.

Surface area of a SPHERE = $4\pi r^2$

curved area of cone (*l* is the slant height)   area of circular base

Surface area of a CONE = $\pi rl + \pi r^2$

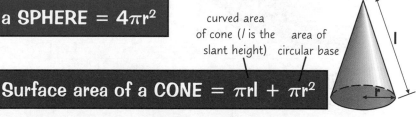

Cylinder

Net of Cylinder

Surface area of a CYLINDER = $2\pi rh + 2\pi r^2$

Note that <u>the length of the rectangle</u> is equal to the <u>circumference</u> of the circular ends.

EXAMPLE: Find the surface area of the cylinder on the right to 1 d.p.

Just put the <u>measurements</u> into the <u>formula</u> and work it out very carefully in stages:

Surface area of cylinder = $2\pi rh + 2\pi r^2$
= $(2 \times \pi \times 1.5 \times 5) + (2 \times \pi \times 1.5^2)$
= 47.123... + 14.137... = 61.261... = 61.3 cm²

1.5 cm

5 cm

Surface area, football, catching friends — nets are so useful...

Get some practice at using those formulas — have a go at these lovely Exam Practice Questions:

Q1   Find the surface area of the cone on the right.   [3 marks]

Q2   Find the radius of a sphere with surface area of 196π cm².   [2 marks]

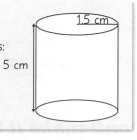

20 cm

5 cm

3D Shapes — Volume

'Still banging on about <u>3D shapes</u>?' you ask. I'm afraid I am. Now it's time to work out their <u>volumes</u>.

LEARN these volume formulas...

Volumes of Cuboids

A <u>cuboid</u> is a <u>rectangular block</u>. Finding its volume is dead easy:

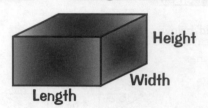

Height

Width

Length

Volume of Cuboid = length × width × height

$$V = L \times W \times H$$

This is the formula for the volume of a <u>cube</u> too — where the <u>length</u>, <u>width</u> and <u>height</u> are all the <u>same</u>.

Volumes of Prisms

A PRISM is a solid (3D) object which is the same shape all the way through — i.e. it has a <u>CONSTANT AREA OF CROSS-SECTION</u>.

Triangular Prism

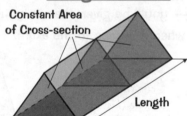

Constant Area of Cross-section

Length

Volume of Prism = cross-sectional area × length

$$V = A \times L$$

 This formula works for <u>any</u> prism.

Cylinder
(circular prism)

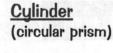

h

r

Constant Area of Cross-section

Volume of Cylinder = area of circle × height

$$V = \pi r^2 h$$

EXAMPLE: Honey comes in cylindrical jars with radius 4.5 cm and height 12 cm.
Dan has a recipe that needs 1 litre of honey. How many jars should he buy?

First, work out the <u>volume</u> of the jar — just use the <u>formula</u> above:

$V = \pi r^2 h = \pi \times 4.5^2 \times 12 = 763.4070...$ cm³

1 litre = 1000 cm³ (see p.66), so he needs to buy **2 jars of honey.**

4.5 cm

12 cm

Honey

Don't make it any more angry — it's already a cross-section...

You might get a question where you're given a shape made up of 1 cm cubes and asked for its volume. All you have to do here is count up the cubes (not forgetting the hidden ones at the back of the shape). Have a go at this Exam Practice Question — you'll need your area formulas from p78.

Q1　Find the volume of the triangular prism on the right. 　[3 marks]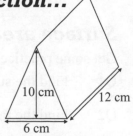

10 cm

12 cm

6 cm

3D Shapes — Volume

Another page on volumes now — my generosity knows no limits.

Volumes of Spheres

$$\text{VOLUME OF SPHERE} = \frac{4}{3}\pi r^3$$

A hemisphere is half a sphere. So the volume of a hemisphere is just half the volume of a full sphere, $V = \frac{2}{3}\pi r^3$.

Volumes of Pyramids and Cones

A pyramid is a shape that goes from a flat base up to a point at the top. Its base can be any shape at all.

 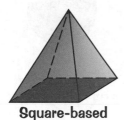

Cone   Square-based Pyramid

$$\text{VOLUME OF PYRAMID} = \frac{1}{3} \times \text{BASE AREA} \times \text{VERTICAL HEIGHT}$$

$$\text{VOLUME OF CONE} = \frac{1}{3} \times \pi r^2 \times h$$

Make sure you use the vertical height in these formulas — don't get confused with the slant height, which you used to find the surface area of a cone.

Volumes of Frustums

A frustum of a cone is what's left when the top part of a cone is cut off parallel to its circular base. You'll be given the formula for the volume of a cone in your exam, but you'll need to remember:

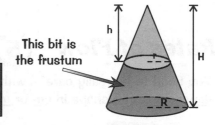

$$\text{VOLUME OF FRUSTUM} = \text{VOLUME OF ORIGINAL CONE} - \text{VOLUME OF REMOVED CONE}$$

This bit is the frustum

EXAMPLE:
A waste paper basket is the shape of a frustum formed by removing the top 10 cm from a cone of height 50 cm and radius 35 cm. Find the volume of the waste paper basket to 3 significant figures.

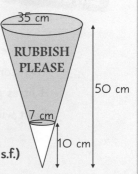

RUBBISH PLEASE

Use the formula for the volume of a cone above:

Volume of original cone = $\frac{1}{3} \times \pi \times 35^2 \times 50 = 64140.850... \text{ cm}^3$

Volume of removed cone = $\frac{1}{3} \times \pi \times 7^2 \times 10 = 513.126... \text{ cm}^3$

Volume of frustum = $64140.850... - 513.126... = 63627.723... = 63600 \text{ cm}^3$ (3 s.f.)

No, a cone isn't 'just as good' — all the other Pharaohs will laugh...

A common mistake is that a frustum is actually called a frustRum. (Yes, I thought this. It blew my mind).

Q1   A cone has radius 12 m and vertical height 18 m. A cone 3 m high with a radius of 2 m is cut off the cone to make a frustum. Find the volume of the frustum, leaving your answer in terms of π.   [4 marks]

3D Shapes — Volume

You might get a question asking you something a little more challenging than just finding the volume — this page will talk you through a couple of <u>trickier types</u> of volume question.

Ratios of Volumes

1) You might need to look at how the <u>volumes</u> of different shapes are linked.

2) So you could be given two shapes and have to show <u>how many times bigger</u> one volume is than the other, or you might need to show the <u>ratio</u> of their volumes:

> ① Work out each volume <u>separately</u> — make sure the <u>units</u> are the <u>same</u>.
> ② Write the volumes as a <u>ratio</u> and <u>simplify</u>.

EXAMPLE:

The cone in the diagram has a radius of 5 cm and a height of 12 cm. The sphere has a radius of 15 cm. Find the ratio of their volumes in its simplest form.

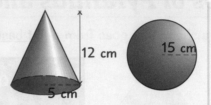

Put the numbers into the <u>volume formulas</u> (see p.83):

Volume of cone $= \frac{1}{3} \times \pi r^2 \times h = \frac{1}{3} \times \pi \times 5^2 \times 12 = \frac{1}{3} \times \pi \times 300 = 100\pi$ cm^3

Volume of sphere $= \frac{4}{3}\pi r^3 = \frac{4}{3} \times \pi \times 15^3 = \frac{4 \times 3375}{3} \times \pi = 4500\pi$ cm^3

When comparing volumes, it's usually best to leave your answers in terms of π.

Find the <u>ratio</u> of the volumes and <u>simplify</u>: volume of cone : volume of sphere

$\div 100\pi \Big(\begin{array}{c} 100\pi : 4500\pi \\ 1:45 \end{array} \Big) \div 100\pi$

Rates of Flow

You need to be really careful with <u>units</u> in rates of flow questions. You might be given the <u>dimensions</u> of a shape in <u>cm</u> or <u>m</u> but the <u>rate of flow</u> in <u>litres</u> (e.g. litres per minute).

EXAMPLE: A cube-shaped fish tank with sides of length 30 cm is being filled with water at a rate of 4 litres per minute. How long will it take to fill the fish tank? Give your answer in minutes and seconds. 1 litre = 1000 cm^3

Find the <u>volume</u> of the fish tank: $V = $ (side length)$^3 = 30^3 = 27\,000$ cm^3

Then convert the <u>rate of flow</u> into cm^3/minute — <u>multiply</u> by 1000:

4 litres per minute $= 4 \times 1000 = 4000$ cm^3/min

So it will take $27\,000 \div 4000 = 6.75$ minutes

= **6 minutes and 45 seconds** to fill the fish tank.

All these mentions of cones are making me want an ice cream...

Sorry — I know it's not the loveliest of pages. Take a calming breath, then have a go at these questions:

Q1 A sphere has a radius of 3 cm. A cylinder has a radius of 6 cm and a height of 10 cm. Show that the volume of the cylinder is 10 times as big as the volume of the sphere. [3 marks]

Q2 A square-based pyramid with base sides of length 60 cm and height 110 cm is being filled with water at a rate of 100 cm^3 per second. Does it take longer than 20 minutes to fill? [3 marks]

Projections

Projections are just different <u>views</u> of a 3D solid shape — looking at it from the <u>front</u>, the <u>side</u> and the <u>top</u>.

The Three Different Projections

There are three different types of projections — <u>front elevations</u>, <u>side elevations</u> and <u>plans</u> (elevation is just another word for projection).

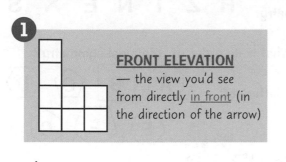

❶ **FRONT ELEVATION**
— the view you'd see from directly <u>in front</u> (in the direction of the arrow)

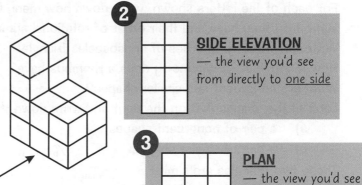

❷ **SIDE ELEVATION**
— the view you'd see from directly to <u>one side</u>

❸ **PLAN**
— the view you'd see from directly <u>above</u>

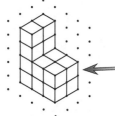

Don't be thrown if you're given a diagram on <u>isometric</u> (dotty) paper like this — it works in just the same way.
If you have to <u>draw</u> shapes on isometric paper, just <u>join the dots</u>.
You should <u>only</u> draw <u>vertical</u> and <u>diagonal</u> lines (no horizontal lines).

Drawing Projections ③

EXAMPLES:

1. The front elevation and plan view of a shape are shown below. Sketch the solid shape.

Front Elevation   Plan View

Just piece together the original shape from the information given — here you get a <u>prism</u> in the shape of the front elevation.

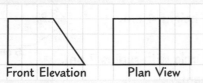

2. a) On the cm square grid, draw the side elevation of the prism from the direction of the arrow.
   b) Draw a plan of the prism on the grid.

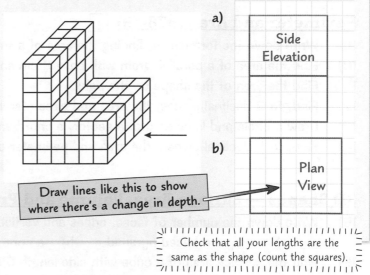

a) Side Elevation

b) Plan View

Draw lines like this to show where there's a change in depth.

Check that all your lengths are the same as the shape (count the squares).

Projections — enough to send you dotty...

Projection questions aren't too bad — just take your time and sketch the diagrams carefully. Watch out for questions on isometric paper — they might look confusing, but they can actually be easier than other questions.

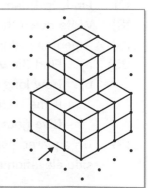

Q1   For the shape on the right, draw:
   a) The front elevation (from the direction of the arrow),   [1 mark]
   b) The side elevation,   [1 mark]
   c) The plan view.   [1 mark]   ③

Section Five — Shapes and Area

Revision Questions for Section Five

There were lots of facts and formulas in that section — time to see if it's all sunk in...

* Try these questions and <u>tick off each one</u> when you <u>get it right</u>.
* When you've done <u>all the questions</u> for a topic and are <u>completely happy</u> with it, tick off the topic.

2D Shapes (p72-75) ☑

1) For each of the letters shown, write down how many lines of symmetry they have and their order of rotational symmetry.

H Z T N E X S ☐

2) Write down four properties of an isosceles triangle. ☐
3) How many lines of symmetry does a rhombus have? What is its order of rotational symmetry? ☐
4) What are congruent and similar shapes? ☐
5) Look at the shapes A-G on the right and write down the letters of:

   a) a pair of congruent shapes,

   b) a pair of similar shapes.

   Ⓐ Ⓑ Ⓒ Ⓓ

   Ⓔ Ⓕ Ⓖ ☐

6) These two triangles are similar.
   Write down the values of b and y.

   $b°$ 6 cm 8 cm $54°$ 37° 10 cm

   89° 3 cm 4 cm $54°$ 37° y cm ☐

Transformations (p76-77) ☑

7) Describe the transformation that maps:

   a) Shape A onto shape B

   b) Shape A onto shape C ☐

8) Carry out the following transformations on the triangle X, which has vertices (1, 1), (4, 1) and (2, 3):

   a) a rotation of 90° clockwise about (1, 1)   b) a translation by the vector $\binom{-3}{-4}$

   c) an enlargement of scale factor 2, centre (1, 1) ☐

Perimeter and Area (p78-79) ☑

9) Write down the formula for finding the area of a trapezium. ☐
10) Find the area of a parallelogram with base 9 cm and vertical height 4 cm. ☐
11) Find the area of the shape on the right. ☐

    3 cm 8 cm 5 cm

12) Find, to 2 decimal places, the area and circumference of a circle with radius 7 cm. ☐
13) Draw a circle and label an arc, a sector, a chord and a segment. ☐
14) Find, to 2 decimal places, the area and perimeter of a quarter circle with radius 3 cm. ☐

3D Shapes — Surface Area, Volume and Projections (p80-85) ☑

15) Write down the number of faces, edges and vertices for the following 3D shapes:

    a) a square-based pyramid   b) a cone   c) a triangular prism. ☐

16) Find the surface area of a cube with side length 5 cm. ☐
17) Find, to 1 decimal place, the surface area of a cylinder with height 8 cm and radius 2 cm. ☐
18) Write down the formula for the volume of a cylinder with radius r and height h. ☐
19) A pentagonal prism has a cross-sectional area of 24 cm² and a length of 15 cm. Find its volume. ☐
20) a) Find the volume of the cylinder on the right (to 2 d.p.).

    9 cm 2 cm

    b) How long will it take to fill the cylinder with water
    if the water is flowing at 1.5 litres per minute?
    Give your answer in seconds to 1 d.p. ☐

21) On squared paper, draw the front elevation (from the direction of the arrow),
    side elevation and plan view of the shape on the right. ☐

Angle Basics

Before we really get going with the thrills and chills of angles and geometry, there are a few things you need to know. Nothing too scary — just some special angles and some fancy notation.

Fancy Angle Names

Some angles have special names. You might have to identify these angles in the exam.

 **ACUTE** angles

Sharp pointy ones
(less than 90°)

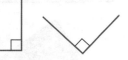 **RIGHT** angles

Square corners
(exactly 90°)

 **OBTUSE** angles

Flatter ones
(between 90° and 180°)

 **REFLEX** angles

Ones that bend
back on themselves
(more than 180°)

Measuring Angles with a Protractor

1) **ALWAYS** position the protractor with the base line of it along one of the lines as shown here:

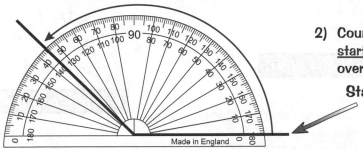
Made in England

2) Count the angle in **10° STEPS** from the start line right round to the other line over there.

Start line

Check your measurement by looking at it. If it's between a right angle and a straight line, it's between 90° and 180°.

DON'T JUST READ A NUMBER OFF THE SCALE — chances are it'll be the wrong one because there are **TWO** scales to choose from.

The answer here is 135° (NOT 45°) which you will only get right if you start counting 10°, 20°, 30°, 40° etc. from the start line until you reach the other line.

Three-Letter Angle Notation

The best way to say which angle you're talking about in a diagram is by using **THREE** letters.
For example in the diagram, angle ACB = 25°.

1) The middle letter is where the angle is.
2) The other two letters tell you which two lines enclose the angle.

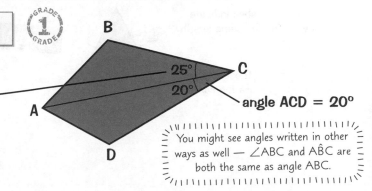

25°
20°
angle ACD = 20°

You might see angles written in other ways as well — $\angle ABC$ and $A\hat{B}C$ are both the same as angle ABC.

If you were an angle you'd be acute one...

If an exam question asks you to write down the 'special name' for a particular angle, don't put 'honeybunch' — they want one of the fancy names above. Learn the page then have a bash at this Exam Practice Question.

Q1   a) An angle measures 66°. What type of angle is this?   [1 mark]
      b) Measure $\angle$ADC on the diagram above.   [1 mark]

Five Angle Rules

If you know <u>all</u> these rules <u>thoroughly</u>, you'll at least have a fighting chance of working out problems with lines and angles. If you don't — you've no chance. Sorry to break it to you like that.

5 Simple Rules — that's all

1) Angles in a <u>triangle</u> add up to <u>180°</u>.

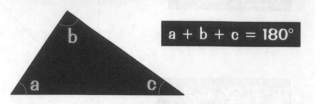

$$a + b + c = 180°$$

There's a nice proof of this (using <u>parallel lines</u>) on the next page.

2) Angles on a <u>straight line</u> add up to <u>180°</u>.

$$a + b + c = 180°$$

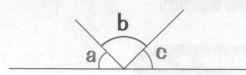

3) Angles in a <u>quadrilateral</u> add up to <u>360°</u>.

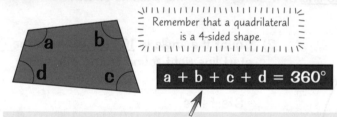

Remember that a quadrilateral is a 4-sided shape.

$$a + b + c + d = 360°$$

You can <u>see why</u> this is if you split the quadrilateral into <u>two triangles</u> along a <u>diagonal</u>. Each triangle has angles adding up to 180°, so the two together have angles adding up to 180° + 180° = 360°.

4) Angles <u>round a point</u> add up to <u>360°</u>.

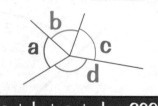

$$a + b + c + d = 360°$$

5) <u>Isosceles triangles</u> have <u>2 sides the same</u> and <u>2 angles the same</u>.

In an isosceles triangle, you only need to know <u>one angle</u> to be able to find the other two.

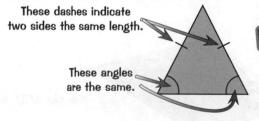

These dashes indicate two sides the same length.

These angles are the same.

EXAMPLE: Find the size of angle x.

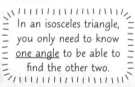

180° − 40° = 140°

<u>The two angles on the right are the same</u> (they're both x) and they must add up to 140°, so $2x = 140°$, which means $x = 70°$.

The first rule of angle club is "you don't talk about angle club"...

All the basic facts are pretty easy really, but examiners like to combine them in questions to confuse you. There are some examples of these on p.90, but have a go at this one as a warm-up.

Q1   Find the size of the angle marked x.   [2 marks]

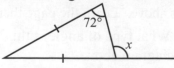

Parallel Lines

Parallel lines are always the <u>same distance apart</u>. This page is all about them.

Angles Around Parallel Lines

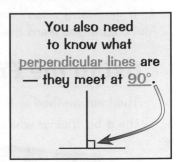
You also need
to know what
<u>perpendicular lines</u> are
— they meet at <u>90°</u>.

When a line crosses two <u>parallel lines</u>...

1) The two bunches of angles are <u>the same</u>.
2) There are <u>only two</u> different angles: <u>a small one</u> and <u>a big one</u>.
3) These <u>ALWAYS ADD UP TO 180°</u>. E.g. 30° and 150° below.

The two lines with the <u>arrows</u> on are <u>parallel</u>:

These are <u>vertically opposite</u> angles.
They're equal to each other.

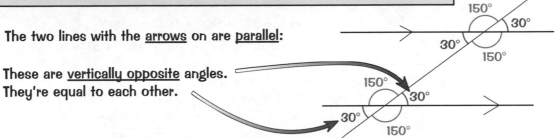

Alternate, Allied and Corresponding Angles

Watch out for these '<u>Z</u>', '<u>C</u>', '<u>U</u>' and '<u>F</u>' shapes popping up.
They're a dead giveaway that you've got a pair of <u>parallel lines</u>.

Don't call them Z, C, U and
F angles in the exam — you'll
need to use their proper names.

ALTERNATE ANGLES

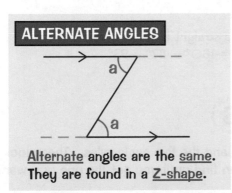

<u>Alternate</u> angles are the <u>same</u>.
They are found in a <u>Z-shape</u>.

ALLIED ANGLES

$a + b = 180°$

<u>Allied</u> angles <u>add up to 180°</u>.
They are found in a <u>C- or U-shape</u>.

CORRESPONDING ANGLES

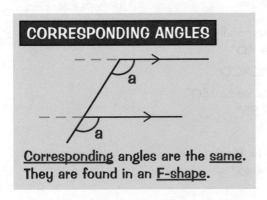

<u>Corresponding</u> angles are the <u>same</u>.
They are found in an <u>F-shape</u>.

EXAMPLE: Prove that the angles in a
triangle add up to 180°.

This is the proof of <u>rule 1</u> from the previous page.
First, draw a <u>triangle</u> between two <u>parallel lines</u>:

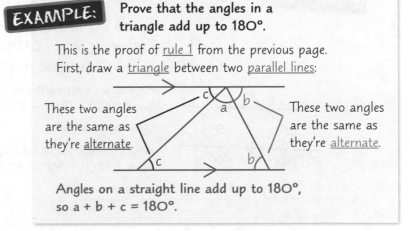

These two angles
are the same as
they're <u>alternate</u>.

These two angles
are the same as
they're <u>alternate</u>.

Angles on a straight line add up to 180°,
so $a + b + c = 180°$.

Looking for Zs isn't a real excuse to sleep in class...

The key to being ace at parallel lines is looking out for those Z, C, U and F shapes.
If you spot one of those, you're onto a winner. When you're ready, try this:

Q1   Find the value of x in the diagram to the right.   [2 marks] ③

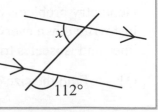

Geometry Problems

As if geometry wasn't enough of a problem already, here's a page dedicated to geometry problems. Make sure you learn the five angle rules on p.88 — they'll help a lot on these questions. Pinky promise.

Using the Five Angle Rules

The best method is to find <u>whatever angles you can</u> until you can work out the ones you're looking for. It's a bit trickier when you have to use <u>more than one</u> rule, but writing them all down is a big help.

EXAMPLES:

1. Find the value of x.

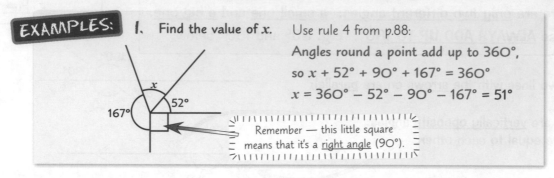

Use rule 4 from p.88:

Angles round a point add up to 360°,

so $x + 52° + 90° + 167° = 360°$

$x = 360° - 52° - 90° - 167° = 51°$

Remember — this little square means that it's a <u>right angle</u> (90°).

2. Find the size of angle CDE.

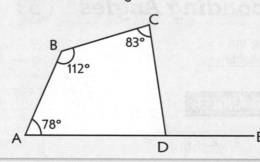

First use rule 3 from p.88:

Angles in a quadrilateral add up to 360°, so the fourth angle in the quadrilateral is $360° - 78° - 112° - 83° = 87°$

Then use rule 2:

Angles on a straight line add up to 180°. So $\angle CDE = 180° - 87° = 93°$

Parallel Lines and Angle Rules

Sometimes you'll come across questions <u>combining</u> parallel lines and the five angle rules. These look pretty tricky, but like always, just work out all the angles you can find until you get the one you want.

EXAMPLE:

Find the value of angle x on the diagram below.

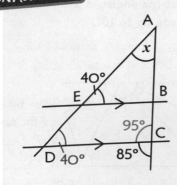

$\angle AEB$ and $\angle ADC$ are corresponding angles, so they are equal. $\angle ADC = 40°$

Use rule 2 from p.88 to find $\angle ACD$:

Angles on a straight line add up to 180°. So $\angle ACD = 180° - 85° = 95°$

Use rule 1 to find x:

Angles in a triangle add up to 180°. So $x = 180° - 95° - 40° = 45°$

It's always a good idea to <u>label</u> your diagram as you work out each angle.

Heaven must be missing an angle...

Geometry problems often look a lot worse than they are — don't panic, just write down everything you can work out. Watch out for hidden parallel lines and isosceles triangles — they can help you work out angles.

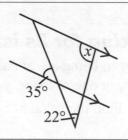

Q1   Find the size of missing angle x.   [2 marks] (3)

Angles in Polygons

A polygon is a <u>many-sided shape</u>, and can be <u>regular</u> or <u>irregular</u>. A regular polygon (p.72) is one where all the sides and angles are the <u>same</u>. By the end of this page you'll be able to work out the angles in them. Wowzers.

Exterior and Interior Angles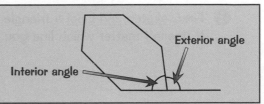

You need to know <u>what</u> exterior and interior angles are and <u>how to find them</u>.

For <u>ANY POLYGON</u> (regular or irregular):

SUM OF EXTERIOR ANGLES = 360°

INTERIOR ANGLE = 180° – EXTERIOR ANGLE

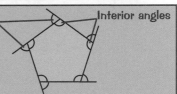

For <u>REGULAR POLYGONS</u> only:

$$\textbf{EXTERIOR ANGLE} = \frac{360°}{n}$$ (n is the number of sides)

EXAMPLE: Find the exterior and interior angles of a regular octagon.

Octagons have 8 sides: exterior angle $= \dfrac{360°}{n} = \dfrac{360°}{8} = 45°$

Use the exterior angle to find the interior angle: interior angle = 180° – exterior angle
$$= 180° - 45° = 135°$$

The Tricky One — Sum of Interior Angles

This formula for the <u>sum of the interior angles</u> works for <u>ALL</u> polygons, even irregular ones:

SUM OF INTERIOR ANGLES = (n – 2) × 180°

EXAMPLE: Find the <u>sum of the interior angles</u> of the polygon on the right.

The polygon is a hexagon, so n = 6: Sum of interior angles = (n − 2) × 180°
$$= (6 - 2) × 180° = 720°$$

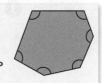

Don't panic if those pesky examiners put algebra in an interior angle question. It looks worse than it is.

EXAMPLE: Find the value of x in the diagram on the right.

First, find the <u>sum of the interior angles</u> of the 5-sided shape:

Sum of interior angles = (n − 2) × 180°
$$= (5 - 2) × 180° = 540°$$

Now write an equation and solve it to find x:
$2x + x + 2x + x + (x + 50°) = 540°$
$7x + 50° = 540° \rightarrow 7x = 490° \rightarrow x = 70°$

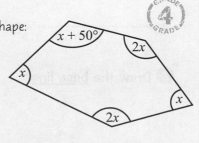

EXCLUSIVE: Heptagon lottery winner — "I'm just a regular guy"…

Learn all the formulas above, and remember whether they go with regular or irregular polygons.

Q1   Find the size of the interior angle of a regular decagon.   [2 marks]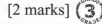

Q2   A regular polygon has exterior angles of 72°. What is the name of the polygon?   [2 marks]

Triangle Construction

How you construct a triangle depends on what <u>info you're given</u> about the triangle...

Three sides — Use a Ruler and Compasses

EXAMPLE: Construct the triangle ABC where AB = 6 cm, BC = 4 cm, AC = 5 cm.

1 First, <u>sketch and label</u> a triangle so you know roughly what's needed. It doesn't matter which line you make the base line.

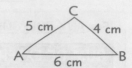

2 Draw the <u>base line</u>. <u>Label</u> the ends A and B.

3 For AC, set the <u>compasses</u> to <u>5 cm</u>, put the point at A and <u>draw an arc</u>.
For BC, set the compasses to <u>4 cm</u>, put the point at B and <u>draw an arc</u>.

4 Where the <u>arcs cross</u> is <u>point C</u>. Now you can finish your triangle.

Sides and Angles — use a Ruler and Protractor

EXAMPLE: Construct triangle DEF. DE = 5 cm, DF = 3 cm, and angle EDF = 40°.

1 <u>Roughly sketch and label</u> the triangle.

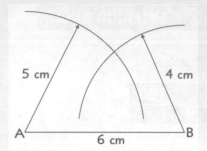

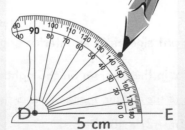

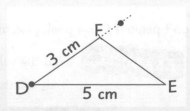

2 Draw the <u>base line</u>.

3 Draw <u>angle EDF</u> (the angle at D) — place the centre of the protractor over D, measure <u>40°</u> and put a dot.

4 Measure <u>3 cm</u> towards the dot and label it F. Join up <u>D and F</u>. Now you've drawn the <u>two sides</u> and the <u>angle</u>. Just join up F and E to <u>complete</u> the triangle.

Compasses at the ready — three, two, one... Construct...

Don't forget to take a pencil, ruler and compasses into the exam. Or you'll look like a plonker.

Q1 Construct an equilateral triangle with sides of 5 cm. Leave visible construction marks. [2 marks]

Q2 Construct a triangle with sides of 3 cm, 4 cm and 6 cm. Leave visible constructions marks. [2 marks]

Loci and Construction

A <u>LOCUS</u> (another ridiculous maths word) is simply:

> ## A LINE or REGION that shows <u>all the points which fit a given rule</u>.

Make sure you learn how to do these <u>PROPERLY</u> using a <u>ruler</u> and <u>compasses</u> as shown on the next few pages.

The Four Different Types of Loci

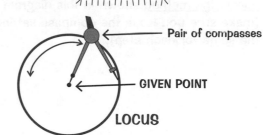

Loci is just the plural of locus.

1) The locus of points which are <u>'A FIXED DISTANCE from a given POINT'</u>.

This locus is simply a <u>CIRCLE</u>.

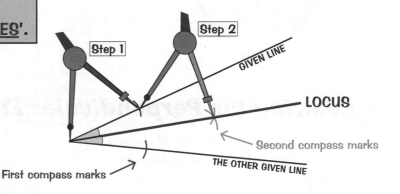

Pair of compasses

GIVEN POINT

LOCUS

2) The locus of points which are <u>'A FIXED DISTANCE from a given LINE'</u>.

This locus is a <u>SAUSAGE SHAPE</u>.

It has <u>straight sides</u> (drawn with a <u>ruler</u>) and <u>ends</u> which are <u>perfect semicircles</u> (drawn with compasses).

Semicircle ends drawn with compasses

GIVEN LINE

LOCUS

3) The locus of points which are <u>'EQUIDISTANT from TWO GIVEN LINES'</u>.

1) Keep the compass setting <u>THE SAME</u> while you make <u>all four marks</u>.

2) Make sure you <u>leave</u> your compass marks <u>showing</u>.

3) You get <u>two equal angles</u> — i.e. this <u>LOCUS</u> is actually an <u>ANGLE BISECTOR</u>.

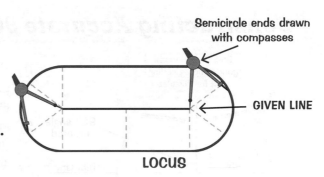

Step 1

Step 2

GIVEN LINE

LOCUS

Second compass marks

THE OTHER GIVEN LINE

First compass marks

4) The locus of points which are <u>'EQUIDISTANT from TWO GIVEN POINTS'</u>.

<u>This LOCUS</u> is all points which are the <u>same distance</u> from A as they are from B.

This time the locus is actually the <u>PERPENDICULAR BISECTOR</u> of the line joining the two points.

(In the diagram below, A and B are the two given points.)

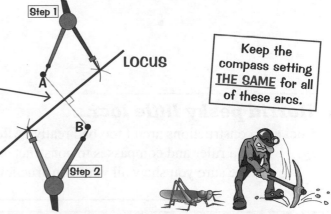

Step 1

LOCUS

A

B

Step 2

Keep the compass setting <u>THE SAME</u> for all of these arcs.

The perpendicular bisector of line segment AB is a line at <u>right angles</u> to AB, passing through the <u>midpoint</u> of AB. This is the method to use if you're asked to draw it.

Loci and Construction

Don't just read the page through once and hope you'll remember it — get your ruler, compasses and pencil out and have a go. It's the only way of testing whether you really know this stuff.

Constructing Accurate 60° Angles

1) They may well ask you to draw an <u>accurate 60° angle</u> without a protractor.

2) <u>Follow the method</u> shown in this diagram (make sure you leave the compass settings the <u>same</u> for each step).

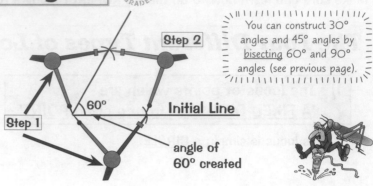

You can construct 30° angles and 45° angles by <u>bisecting</u> 60° and 90° angles (see previous page).

Step 2

60°

Step 1

Initial Line

angle of 60° created

Constructing Accurate 90° Angles

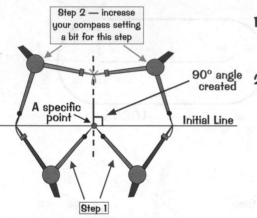

Step 2 — increase your compass setting a bit for this step

90° angle created

A specific point

Initial Line

Step 1

1) They might want you to construct an <u>accurate 90° angle</u>.

2) Make sure you can <u>follow the method</u> shown in this diagram.

The examiners <u>WON'T</u> accept any of these constructions done 'by eye' or with a protractor. You've got to do them the <u>PROPER WAY</u>, with <u>compasses</u>. <u>DON'T</u> rub out your compass marks, or the examiner won't know you used the proper method.

Drawing the Perpendicular From a Point to a Line

1) This is similar to the one above but <u>not quite the same</u> — make sure you can do <u>both</u>.

2) You'll be given a line and a point, like this:

A ——————— B

•

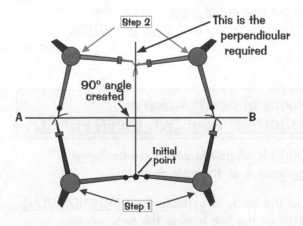

Step 2

This is the perpendicular required

90° angle created

A ——————————————— B

Initial point

Step 1

Horrid pesky little loci...

Loci and constructions aren't too bad really. After all, you get to draw nd use compasses and stuff.

Q1   Use a ruler and compasses to construct an accurate 60° angle at T.
Make sure you show all your construction lines.   [2 marks]

T ————————————————

Section Six — Angles and Geometry

Loci and Construction — Worked Examples

After all that learning it must be time for a break, right? Wrong. There will be time for tea and biscuits later. For now it's all about learning how to put all those crazy constructions to good use.

EXAMPLES:

1. A farmer wants to place a fence around his chicken coop.
It should be exactly 2 m from the coop on all sides.
Using a scale of 1 cm = 1 m, draw where the fence should go.

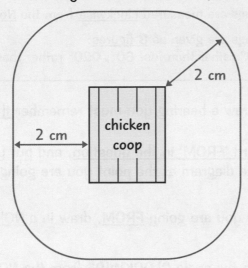

1) 1 cm = 1 m, so 2 m = 2 cm.

2) Set your compasses to 2 cm.

3) Place the point on each <u>corner</u> and draw a <u>quarter-circle</u> at each one.

4) Draw lines <u>parallel</u> to each edge of the chicken coop 2 cm away, joining up the ends of the quarter-circles.

2. Point P lies somewhere in triangle ABC.
Shade the area in which P could lie, given that:

P is at least 4 cm away from A.
P is closer to B than C.

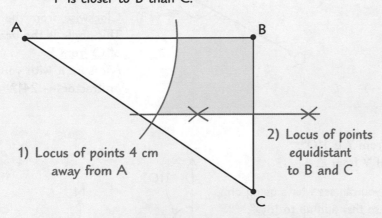

1) Locus of points 4 cm away from A

2) Locus of points equidistant to B and C

1) Set your compasses to 4 cm. Place the point on A and draw an <u>arc</u>.

2) Draw the <u>perpendicular bisector</u> of line BC using the method given on page 93.

3) <u>Shade</u> the area that's at least 4 cm away from A and closer to B than C.

> Always <u>leave your construction lines showing</u>.
> They show the examiner that you used the proper method.

Stay at least 3 m away from point C — or I'll release the hounds...

I can't stress this enough — make sure you draw your diagrams ACCURATELY (using a ruler and a pair of compasses). Now try this practice question:

Q1 In a stately home, visitors must stay at least 2 m away from the portrait and at least 2 m away from the statue. Make a copy of the diagram using a scale of 1 cm = 1 m and indicate the area where visitors can go. [4 marks]

Bearings

Bearings. They'll be useful next time you're off sailing. Or in your Maths exam.

Bearings

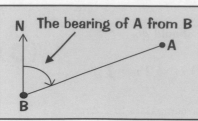

1) A bearing is just a <u>direction</u> given as an <u>angle</u> in degrees.

2) All bearings are measured <u>clockwise</u> from the <u>North line</u>.

3) All bearings are given as *3 figures*:
e.g. 060° rather than just 60°, 020° rather than 20° etc.

The 3 Key Words

To find or draw a bearing you must remember <u>three key words</u>:

① 'FROM' <u>Find the word 'FROM' in the question</u>, and put your pencil on the diagram at the point you are going '<u>from</u>'.

② NORTH LINE At the point you are going <u>FROM</u>, draw in a <u>NORTH LINE</u>.

③ CLOCKWISE Now draw in the angle <u>CLOCKWISE</u> from the <u>NORTH LINE</u> to the <u>line joining the two points</u> — this angle is the <u>bearing</u>.

EXAMPLES:

1. Find the bearing of Q <u>from P</u>.

1) 'From P'
2) North line at P
3) Clockwise, from the N-line. This angle is the bearing of <u>Q from P</u>. Measure it with your protractor — 241°.

2. The bearing of Z from Y is 110°. Find the bearing of Y from Z.

First sketch a diagram so you can see what's going on. Angles a and b are <u>allied</u>, so they add up to <u>180°</u>.

 See page 89 for allied angles.

Angle b = 180° − 110° = 70°
So bearing of Y from Z = 360° − 70° = 290°.

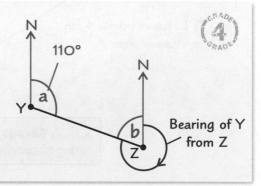

Please bear with me while I figure out where we are...

Learn the three key points above and scribble them out from memory. Now try these practice questions.

Q1 Measure the bearing of T from H. 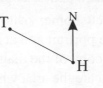 [1 mark]

Q2 A man walks in a straight line from A to B on a bearing of 210°. What bearing should he travel on to walk straight from B to A? [2 marks]

Section Six — Angles and Geometry

Maps and Scale Drawings

<u>Scales</u> tell you what a <u>distance</u> on a <u>map</u> or <u>drawing</u> represents in <u>real life</u>. They can be written in various ways, but they all boil down to something like "<u>1 cm represents 5 km</u>".

Map Scales

> 1 cm = 3 km   — "1 cm represents 3 km"
>
> 1 : 2000   — 1 cm on the map means 2000 cm in real life.
>   Converting to m gives "1 cm represents 20 m".
>
> ⊢——————⊣   Use a ruler — the line's 2 cm long, so 2 cm means 1 km.
> 0   km   1   Dividing by 2 gives "1 cm represents 0.5 km".

To <u>convert</u> between <u>maps</u> and <u>real life</u>, <u>learn</u> these rules:

- Make sure your map scale is of the form "<u>1 cm = ...</u>"
- To find <u>REAL-LIFE</u> distances, <u>MULTIPLY</u> by the <u>MAP SCALE</u>.
- To find <u>MAP</u> distances, <u>DIVIDE</u> by the <u>MAP SCALE</u>.
- Always check your answer looks <u>sensible</u>.

Converting from Map Distance to Real Life — Multiply

EXAMPLE:

This map shows the original Roman M6 motorway built by the Emperor Hadrian in the year AD 120. Work out the length of the section of the M6 between Wigan and Preston in km.

1) Measure with a <u>ruler</u>:   Distance on map = 2 cm

2) Read off the <u>scale</u>:   Scale is 1 cm = 12 km

3) For <u>real life, multiply</u>:   Real distance is: 2 × 12 = **24 km**

This looks <u>sensible</u>. ✓

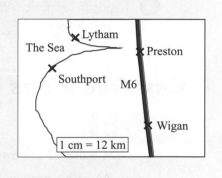

Converting from Real Life to Map Distance — Divide

EXAMPLE:

Helmsley is 18 km west of Pickering.

a) How far apart would they be on this map?

     Real-life distance = 18 km

     Scale is 1 cm = 6 km

<u>Divide</u> for a — Distance on map = 18 ÷ 6 = **3 cm**
<u>map distance</u>.

This looks <u>sensible</u>. ✓

b) Mark Helmsley on the map.

<u>Measure</u> 3 cm to the <u>west</u> (left) of Pickering:

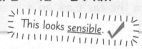

Follow this map of the road to exam glory... What?... Cheesy?... Me?

Give these practice questions a go once you're happy with the two formulas and know when to use them.

Q1   Use this map to find the distance between Broughton and Coniston in miles.   [2 marks]

Q2   Sarah's house is 2.25 km away from Luke's house. How far apart in cm would they be on a map where 1 cm represents 500 m?   [2 marks]

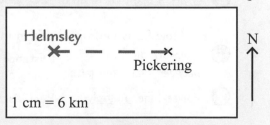

Maps and Scale Drawings

Scale Drawings

Scale drawings work just like maps. To convert between real life and scale drawings, just replace the word 'map' with 'drawing' in the rules on the previous page.

EXAMPLE:

This is a scale drawing of a room in Clare's house. 1 cm represents 1.5 m.

a) Find the real length and width of the sofa in m.

① Measure with a ruler.   Length on drawing = 2 cm
Width on drawing = 0.5 cm

② Multiply to get real-life length.   Real length = 2 × 1.5 = 3 m
Real width = 0.5 × 1.5 = 0.75 m

b) Clare's dining table is 90 cm wide and 180 cm long. Draw the table on the scale drawing.

① Scale uses m, so convert cm to m.   Width = 90 cm = 0.9 m
Length = 180 cm = 1.8 m

② Divide to get scale drawing length.   Width on drawing = 0.9 ÷ 1.5 = 0.6 cm
Length on drawing = 1.8 ÷ 1.5 = 1.2 cm

③ Draw with a ruler in any sensible position and label.

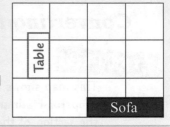

Map Questions Using Bearings

EXAMPLE:

Liam walks 1.2 km from the car park on a bearing of 120°.

a) Mark his position on the map.

① Work out how many km 1 cm represents.   1 cm = 20 000 cm
= 200 m = 0.2 km. So 1 cm = 0.2 km

② Divide to get distance on map.   Distance walked on map = 1.2 ÷ 0.2
= 6 cm

③ Mark a point 6 cm away, 120° clockwise from the North line.

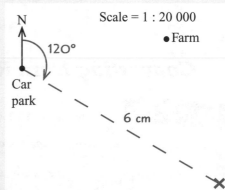

b) How far is he from the farm in km?

① Measure distance between Liam and farm.   Distance between Liam and farm = 4 cm

② For real life, multiply: Real distance = 4 × 0.2 = 0.8 km

Well, you should have got your bearings on map scales by now...

Keep your ruler and protractor handy when you're doing map and scale drawing questions.

Q1 This is a scale drawing of a park. What does 1 cm represent? Mark on an area of woodland with dimensions 250 m × 300 m.
[3 marks]

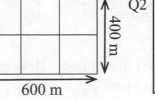

Q2 A cinema is on a bearing of 035° from Ellie's house and is 5 miles away. Mark the cinema on this map.
[3 marks]

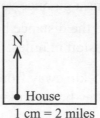

Pythagoras' Theorem

Once upon a time there lived a clever chap called Pythagoras. He came up with a clever theorem...

Pythagoras' Theorem is Used on Right-Angled Triangles

Pythagoras' theorem only works for <u>RIGHT-ANGLED TRIANGLES</u>.
It uses <u>two sides</u> to find the <u>third side</u>.

The formula for Pythagoras' theorem is:

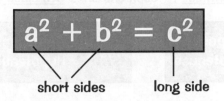

$$a^2 + b^2 = c^2$$

short sides   long side

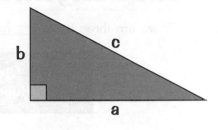

The trouble is, the formula can be quite difficult to use. <u>Instead</u>, it's a lot better to just <u>remember</u> these <u>three simple steps</u>, which work every time:

1) SQUARE THEM   <u>SQUARE THE TWO NUMBERS</u> that you are given,
(use the x^2 button if you've got your calculator.)

2) ADD or SUBTRACT   To find the <u>longest side</u>, <u>ADD</u> the two squared numbers. $a^2 + b^2 = c^2$
To find <u>a shorter side</u>, <u>SUBTRACT</u> the smaller from the larger. $c^2 - b^2 = a^2$

3) SQUARE ROOT   Once you've got your answer, take the <u>SQUARE ROOT</u> $c = \sqrt{a^2 + b^2}$
(use the $\sqrt{\ }$ button on your calculator). $a = \sqrt{c^2 - b^2}$

EXAMPLES:

1. Find the length of side PQ in this triangle.

1) <u>Square</u> them: $a^2 = 5^2 = 25$, $b^2 = 12^2 = 144$

2) You want to find the <u>longest side</u>, so <u>ADD</u>: $a^2 + b^2 = c^2$
     $25 + 144 = 169$

3) <u>Square root</u>: $c = \sqrt{169} = 13$ cm ←

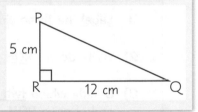

Always check the answer's <u>sensible</u> — <u>13 cm</u> is longer than the other two sides, but not too much longer, so it seems OK.

2. Find the length of SU to 1 decimal place.

1) <u>Square</u> them: $b^2 = 3^2 = 9$, $c^2 = 6^2 = 36$

2) You want to find <u>a shorter side</u>, so <u>SUBTRACT</u>: $c^2 - b^2 = a^2$
     $36 - 9 = 27$

3) <u>Square root</u>: $a = \sqrt{27} = 5.196...$
     $= 5.2$ m (to 1 d.p.)

Check the answer is <u>sensible</u> — yes, it's a bit shorter than the longest side.

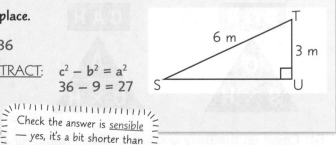

Remember, if it's not a right angle, it's a wrong angle...

Once you've learned all the Pythagoras facts on this page, try these Exam Practice Questions.

Q1   Find the length of AC correct to 1 decimal place.   [3 marks]

Q2   A 4 m long ladder leans against a wall. Its base is 1.2 m from the wall.
How far up the wall does the ladder reach? Give your answer to 1 decimal place.   [3 marks]

Trigonometry — Sin, Cos, Tan

Trigonometry — it's clever stuff. The three trig formulas are used on right-angled triangles to:
a) find an unknown side if you know a side and an angle, or b) find an angle if you know two lengths.

The 3 Trigonometry Formulas

There are three basic <u>trig formulas</u> — each one links <u>two sides and an angle</u> of a <u>right-angled triangle</u>.

$$\text{Sin } x = \frac{\text{Opposite}}{\text{Hypotenuse}}$$

$$\text{Cos } x = \frac{\text{Adjacent}}{\text{Hypotenuse}}$$

$$\text{Tan } x = \frac{\text{Opposite}}{\text{Adjacent}}$$

- The <u>Hypotenuse</u> is the <u>LONGEST SIDE</u>.

- The <u>Opposite</u> is the side <u>OPPOSITE</u> the angle <u>being used</u> (x).

- The <u>Adjacent</u> is the (other) side <u>NEXT TO</u> the angle <u>being used</u>.

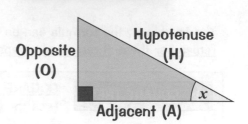

Formula Triangles Make Things Easier

There's more about formula triangles on p.69 if you need to jog your memory.

A great way to tackle trig questions is to convert the formulas into <u>formula triangles</u>.
Then you can use the <u>same method every time</u>, no matter which side or angle is being asked for.

1) <u>Label</u> the three sides <u>O, A and H</u> (Opposite, Adjacent and Hypotenuse).

2) Write down '<u>SOH CAH TOA</u>'.

3) Decide which <u>two sides</u> are <u>involved</u>: O,H A,H or O,A
and choose <u>SOH</u>, <u>CAH</u> or <u>TOA</u> accordingly.

4) Turn the one you choose into a <u>FORMULA TRIANGLE</u>:

In the formula triangles, S represents sin x, C is cos x, and T is tan x.

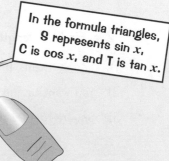

5) <u>Cover up</u> the thing you want to find with your finger,
and write down whatever is left showing.

6) <u>Stick in the numbers</u> and work it out using the
[sin] , [cos] and [tan] buttons on your <u>calculator</u>.

If you're finding an <u>angle</u>, you'll need to add an extra step to find the <u>inverse</u>. See next page.

SOH CAH TOA — the not-so-secret formula for success...

Trigonometry? In a foundation book? It's health and safety gone mad. Just make sure you remember
SOH CAH TOA and know the formula triangles. Then its just a matter of bunging the numbers in.

Trigonometry — Examples

Here are some lovely examples using the method from the previous page to help you through the trials of trig.

Examples:

---

1   Find the length of x in the triangle to the right.

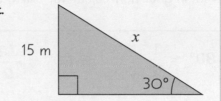

1) **Label** the sides ——
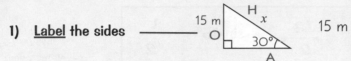

2) **Write down** —— (SOH) CAH TOA

3) **O** and **H** involved

4) Write down the **formula triangle** ——
```
    O
  -----
  S × H
```

5) **You want H** so **cover it up** to give —— $H = \dfrac{O}{S}$

6) **Put in** the **numbers**
[15] [÷] [sin] [30] [=]
$x = \dfrac{15}{\sin 30°} = \dfrac{15}{0.5} = 30 \text{ m}$

---

2   Find the angle x in the triangle to the right.

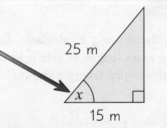

1) **Label** the sides ——

2) **Write down** —— SOH (CAH) TOA

3) **A** and **H** involved

4) Write down the **formula triangle**
```
    A
  -----
  C × H
```

5) You want the **angle** so **cover up C** to give —— $C = \dfrac{A}{H}$

6) **Put in** the numbers
[15] [÷] [25] [=]
$\cos x = \dfrac{15}{25} = 0.6$

7) Find the **inverse.**
[shift] [cos] [0.6] [=]
$\Rightarrow x = \cos^{-1}(0.6) = 53.1301...°$
$= 53.1°$ (1 d.p.)

> When you're finding an **angle** you'll have to find the **INVERSE** at the end. Press [SHIFT] or [2ndF], followed by sin, cos or tan — your calculator will display sin⁻¹, cos⁻¹ or tan⁻¹

I do trigonometry outdoors cos I always get a great sin tan...

Make sure your calculator is in DEG mode before using the sin, cos and tan buttons.

Q1   Find the length of y and give your answer to 2 decimal places.

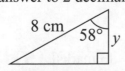

[3 marks]

Q2   Find the value of x and give your answer to 1 decimal place.

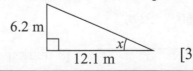

[3 marks]

Section Six — Angles and Geometry

Trigonometry — Common Values

Now that you're in the swing of trigonometry questions it's time to put those calculators away. Sorry.

Learn these Common Trig Values

The tables below contain a load of <u>useful trig values</u>. You might get asked to work out some <u>exact</u> trig answers in your non-calculator exam, so having these in your brain will come in handy.

$$\sin 30° = \frac{1}{2} \qquad \sin 60° = \frac{\sqrt{3}}{2} \qquad \sin 45° = \frac{1}{\sqrt{2}}$$

$$\cos 30° = \frac{\sqrt{3}}{2} \qquad \cos 60° = \frac{1}{2} \qquad \cos 45° = \frac{1}{\sqrt{2}}$$

$$\tan 30° = \frac{1}{\sqrt{3}} \qquad \tan 60° = \sqrt{3} \qquad \tan 45° = 1$$

If you're asked for <u>exact</u> answers, <u>don't</u> convert them to decimals at the end.

$$\tan 0° = 0$$

$$\cos 90° = 0 \qquad \cos 0° = 1$$

$$\sin 90° = 1 \qquad \sin 0° = 0$$

Have a look at the <u>examples</u> below —
they might help cement a few values into your head.

EXAMPLES:

1. Without using a calculator, find the exact length of side b in the right-angled triangle shown.

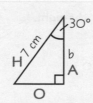

1) It's a right-angled triangle so use SOH CAH TOA to pick the correct <u>trig formula</u> to use.

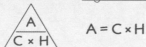 $A = C \times H$

2) Put in the <u>numbers</u> from the diagram in the question.
$$b = \cos 30° \times 7$$

3) You know the <u>value</u> of cos 30°, so <u>substitute</u> this in.
$$b = \frac{\sqrt{3}}{2} \times 7 = \frac{7\sqrt{3}}{2} \text{ cm}$$

2. Without using a calculator, show that
$$\cos 60° + \sin 30° = 1$$

Put in the right values for cos 60° and sin 30°, then do the sum.

$$\cos 60° = \frac{1}{2} \qquad \sin 30° = \frac{1}{2}$$

$$\cos 60° + \sin 30° = \frac{1}{2} + \frac{1}{2} = 1$$

Tri angles — go on, you might like them...
Use the tables to learn the trig values — then, when you're ready, try this Exam Practice Question.

Q1   Find the exact length of side x in each of these triangles.

a)
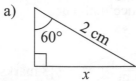
x
[3 marks]

b)
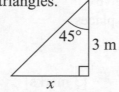
x
[3 marks]

Vectors — Theory

Vectors represent a movement of a certain <u>size</u> in a certain <u>direction</u>.
They might seem a bit weird at first, but there are really just a few facts to get to grips with...

The Vector Notations

There are several ways to <u>write</u> vectors...

They're shown on a diagram by an <u>arrow</u>.

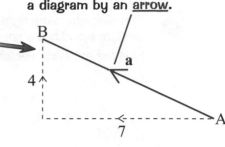

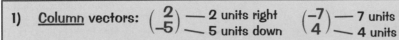

1) <u>Column</u> vectors: $\begin{pmatrix} 2 \\ -5 \end{pmatrix}$ — 2 units right, 5 units down $\begin{pmatrix} -7 \\ 4 \end{pmatrix}$ — 7 units left, 4 units up

2) **a** ——— <u>exam questions</u> use <u>bold</u> like this

3) <u>a</u> ——— <u>you</u> should always <u>underline</u> them

4) $\overrightarrow{AB}$ ——— this means the vector <u>from point A to point B</u>

Multiplying a Vector by a Number

Vectors that are <u>multiples</u> of each other are <u>parallel</u>.

1) Multiplying a vector by a <u>positive</u> number <u>changes</u> the vector's <u>size</u> but <u>not its direction</u>.

2) If the number's <u>negative</u> then the <u>direction gets switched</u>.

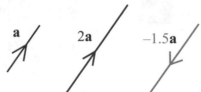

a   2**a**   −1.5**a**

Adding and Subtracting Vectors

You can describe movements between points by <u>adding and subtracting known vectors</u>.

"<u>a</u> + <u>b</u>" means 'go along <u>a</u> then <u>b</u>'.

a + b   R
P
a   **b**
Q

In the diagrams,
$\overrightarrow{PR}$ = <u>a</u> + <u>b</u> and
$\overrightarrow{XZ}$ = <u>c</u> − <u>d</u>.

"<u>c</u> − <u>d</u>" means 'go along c then backwards along d' (the <u>minus</u> sign means go the <u>opposite</u> way).

Y
c
X   **d**
c − d   Z

When adding <u>column vectors</u>, add the top to the top and the bottom to the bottom. The same goes when subtracting. $\begin{pmatrix} 3 \\ -1 \end{pmatrix} + \begin{pmatrix} 5 \\ 3 \end{pmatrix} = \begin{pmatrix} 3+5 \\ -1+3 \end{pmatrix} = \begin{pmatrix} 8 \\ 2 \end{pmatrix}$

Vector directions — In 5p + 2q take a left onto AB...

There are a lot of different ideas to take in on this page, so here's a bit of a warm-up to get you into the swing of things before the proper examples on the next page.

Q1   Calculate $\begin{pmatrix} 4 \\ 7 \end{pmatrix} - \begin{pmatrix} 3 \\ 2 \end{pmatrix}$.   [1 mark]

Q2   Find $\overrightarrow{LN}$ on the diagram to the right.   [1 mark]

M
c   **d**
L   N

Vectors — Examples

What's that I hear you cry? A complicated topic with no examples? Never fear, here's a full page of 'em. Keep an eye on the <u>direction</u> of the arrow and you'll be a fully fledged vectorist in no time.

Examples

 The diagram to the right shows an isometric grid. Vectors **a** and **b** are shown on the grid.

Find the following vectors in terms of **a** and **b**:

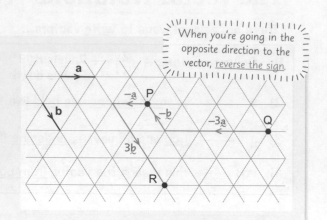

When you're going in the opposite direction to the vector, <u>reverse the sign</u>.

a) $\overrightarrow{PR}$

Use multiples of $\underline{a}$ and $\underline{b}$ to get from <u>P to R</u>.
$\overrightarrow{PR} = -\underline{a} + 3\underline{b}$

b) $\overrightarrow{QP}$

Use multiples of $\underline{a}$ and $\underline{b}$ to get from <u>Q to P</u>.
$\overrightarrow{QP} = -3\underline{a} - \underline{b}$

2. Given that $\mathbf{p} = \begin{pmatrix} 4 \\ -1 \end{pmatrix}$ and $\mathbf{r} = \begin{pmatrix} -3 \\ 2 \end{pmatrix}$ find:

a) $4\mathbf{p}$

$$4 \times \begin{pmatrix} 4 \\ -1 \end{pmatrix} = \begin{pmatrix} 4 \times 4 \\ 4 \times -1 \end{pmatrix} = \begin{pmatrix} 16 \\ -4 \end{pmatrix}$$

b) $-2\mathbf{p} + 4\mathbf{r}$

$$-2 \times \begin{pmatrix} 4 \\ -1 \end{pmatrix} + 4 \times \begin{pmatrix} -3 \\ 2 \end{pmatrix} = \begin{pmatrix} -2 \times 4 \\ -2 \times -1 \end{pmatrix} + \begin{pmatrix} 4 \times -3 \\ 4 \times 2 \end{pmatrix}$$
$$= \begin{pmatrix} -8 \\ 2 \end{pmatrix} + \begin{pmatrix} -12 \\ 8 \end{pmatrix} = \begin{pmatrix} -20 \\ 10 \end{pmatrix}$$

3. The diagram to the right shows the vectors $\overrightarrow{BA}$ and $\overrightarrow{AC}$.

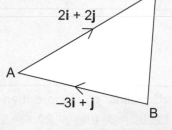

a) Find $\overrightarrow{BC}$ in terms of **i** and **j**.

You need to go from <u>B to A</u>, then from <u>A to C</u>.

$\overrightarrow{BA} = -3\underline{i} + \underline{j}$
$\overrightarrow{AC} = 2\underline{i} + 2\underline{j}$
$\overrightarrow{BC} = -3\underline{i} + \underline{j} + 2\underline{i} + 2\underline{j}$
$\quad\;\; = -\underline{i} + 3\underline{j}$

b) Alison adds a new line, BD, to the diagram. Given that $\overrightarrow{BD}$ is in the opposite direction to $\overrightarrow{BC}$ and is twice the length of $\overrightarrow{BC}$, find $\overrightarrow{BD}$ in terms of **i** and **j**.

$\overrightarrow{BD}$ is in the <u>opposite</u> direction to $\overrightarrow{BC}$, so <u>reverse</u> the sign. $\Longrightarrow \underline{i} - 3\underline{j}$
$\overrightarrow{BD}$ is also <u>twice</u> the length of $\overrightarrow{BC}$, so <u>multiply by 2</u>. $\Longrightarrow 2\underline{i} - 6\underline{j}$
So $\overrightarrow{BD} = 2\underline{i} - 6\underline{j}$

From numpty to vector king — via R, E, V, I, S, I, O and N...

You need to get to grips with questions like the ones above, so here's one to have a go at...

Q1 Find $\overrightarrow{EF}$ in terms of **p** and **q**. [2 marks]

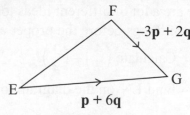

Revision Questions for Section Six

There are lots of opportunities to show off your artistic skills here (as long as you use them to answer the questions).

* Try these questions and <u>tick off each one</u> when you <u>get it right</u>.
* When you've done <u>all the questions</u> for a topic and are <u>completely happy</u> with it, tick off the topic.

<u>Angles and Geometry Problems (p87-90)</u> ☑

1) What is the name for an angle larger than 90° but smaller than 180°?

2) What do angles in a quadrilateral add up to?

3) Find the missing angles in the diagrams below.

a)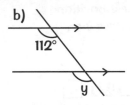

b)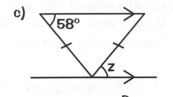

c)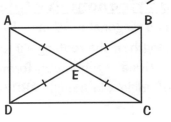

4) Given that angle DAC = 70°, work out angle CED.

<u>Angles in Polygons (p91)</u> ☑

5) Find the exterior angle of a regular hexagon.

6) Find the sum of interior angles in a regular octagon.

7) Find the interior angle of a regular 20-sided polygon.

<u>Constructions and Loci (p92-95)</u> ☐

8) Construct triangle XYZ, where XY = 5.6 cm, XZ = 7.2 cm and angle YXZ = 55°.

9) What shape does the locus of points that are a fixed distance from a given point make?

10) Draw a horizontal line with a length of 8 cm.
Draw the locus of points exactly 2 cm away from the line.

11) Construct an accurate 90° angle.

12) Draw a square with sides of length 6 cm and label it ABCD. Shade the region
that is nearer to AB than CD and less than 4 cm from vertex A.

<u>Bearings (p96)</u> ☐

13) Using the diagram on the right, find the bearing of Y from X.

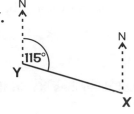

14) Look at the diagram to the right.
Tom wants to travel from point A to point B.
Find the bearing he should travel on.

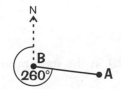

Revision Questions for Section Six

Maps and Scale Drawings (p97-98)

15) The scale on a map is 1 cm = 4 km. On the map, Leadz is 6.5 cm away from Horrowgate. How far is this in real life?

16) The garden plan on the right has a scale of 1:200.
Allen wants to build a square shed in the top right corner of the garden and a rectangular pond in the bottom right.
The shed will measure 4m × 4m and the pond will measure 6m × 2m. Draw these accurately on the plan.

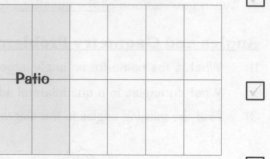

Patio

17) John travels on a bearing of 180° for 3 km.
He travels on a bearing of 145° from his new position for 6 km. Using a scale of 1 cm = 1.5 km, draw an accurate diagram to represent this.

Pythagoras and Trigonometry (p99-102)

18) A rectangle has a diagonal of 15 cm. Its short side is 4 cm.
Calculate the length of the rectangle's long side to 1 d.p.

19) Write down the three trigonometry formula triangles.

20) Find the size of angle x in triangle ABC to 1 d.p.

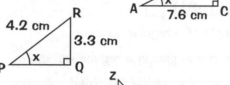

21) Work out the value of x in triangle PQR.

22) Find the exact length of side XZ in triangle XYZ without using your calculator.

23) Without using your calculator, show that $\tan 45° + \sin 60° = \dfrac{2 + \sqrt{3}}{2}$

Vectors (p103-104)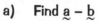

24) $\underset{\sim}{a}$ and $\underset{\sim}{b}$ are column vectors, where $\underset{\sim}{a} = \begin{pmatrix} 4 \\ -2 \end{pmatrix}$ and $\underset{\sim}{b} = \begin{pmatrix} 7 \\ 6 \end{pmatrix}$
   a) Find $\underset{\sim}{a} - \underset{\sim}{b}$
   b) Find $5\underset{\sim}{a}$

25) The diagram to the right shows a grid of unit squares.
Find the vector $\underset{\sim}{c}$ in terms of $\underset{\sim}{a}$ and $\underset{\sim}{b}$.

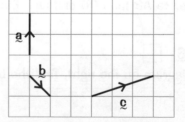

26) Find the vector that describes $\overrightarrow{XY}$ in the form $m\underset{\sim}{a} + n\underset{\sim}{b}$.

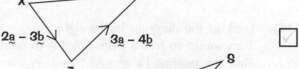

27) Find the vector that describes $\overrightarrow{RS}$ in the form $m\underset{\sim}{i} + n\underset{\sim}{j}$.

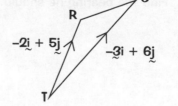

Probability Basics

A lot of people think <u>probability</u> is tough. But learn the <u>basics</u> well, and it'll all make sense.

All Probabilities are Between 0 and 1

- Probabilities are <u>always</u> between 0 and 1.
- The <u>higher</u> the probability of something, the <u>more likely</u> it is.
- A probability of <u>ZERO</u> means it will <u>NEVER HAPPEN</u>.
- A probability of <u>ONE</u> means it <u>DEFINITELY WILL HAPPEN</u>.

You can show the probability of something happening on a <u>scale</u> from 0 to 1.
Probabilities can be given as <u>fractions</u>, <u>decimals</u> or <u>percentages</u>.

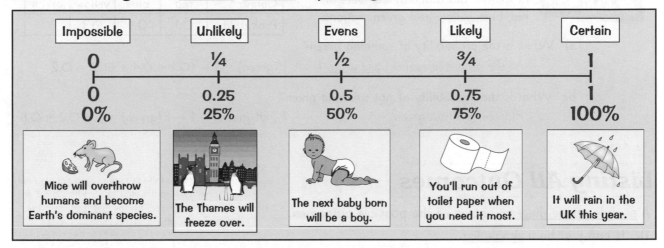

Impossible	Unlikely	Evens	Likely	Certain
0	¼	½	¾	1
0	0.25	0.5	0.75	1
0%	25%	50%	75%	100%

Mice will overthrow humans and become Earth's dominant species.

The Thames will freeze over.

The next baby born will be a boy.

You'll run out of toilet paper when you need it most.

It will rain in the UK this year.

Use This Formula When All Outcomes are Equally Likely

Use this formula to find probabilities for a <u>fair</u> spinner, coin or dice.
A spinner/coin/dice is 'fair' when it's <u>equally likely</u> to land on <u>any</u> of its sides.

$$\text{Probability} = \frac{\text{Number of ways for something to happen}}{\text{Total number of possible outcomes}}$$

<u>Outcomes</u> are just 'things that could happen'.

EXAMPLE: The picture on the right shows a fair, 8-sided spinner.

a) Work out the probability of this spinner landing on green.

There are <u>8 sides</u> so there are <u>8 possible outcomes</u>.
There are <u>3 ways</u> for it to land on <u>green</u>.

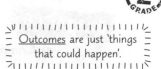

P(green) means 'The probability of the spinner landing on green'.

$$\text{P(green)} = \frac{\text{number of ways for 'green' to happen}}{\text{total number of possible outcomes}} = \frac{3}{8} \text{ (or 0.375)}$$

b) Which of its four colours is the spinner <u>least likely</u> to land on?

It's least likely to land on the colour that 'can happen in the <u>fewest ways</u>' — this is the one on the <u>fewest sections</u>.

Yellow

The probability of this getting you marks in the exam = 1...

You need to know the facts in the boxes above. You also need to know how to <u>use</u> them.

Q1   Calculate the probability of the fair spinner on the right:
      a) landing on a 4.   [2 marks]   b) landing on an even number.   [2 marks]
Q2   Show the probabilities in Q1 on a scale from 0 to 1.   [1 mark]

More Probability

Did someone order another page on probability? Coming right up...

Probabilities Add Up To 1

1) If only one possible result can happen at a time, then the probabilities of all the results add up to 1.

> **Probabilities always ADD UP to 1**

2) So since something must either happen or not happen (i.e. only one of these can happen at a time):

> **P(event happens) + P(event doesn't happen) = 1**

EXAMPLE: A spinner has different numbers of red, blue, yellow and green sections.

Colour	red	blue	yellow	green
Probability	0.1	0.4	0.3	

a) What is the probability of spinning green?

All the probabilities must add up to 1.

P(green) = 1 − (0.1 + 0.4 + 0.3) = 0.2

b) What is the probability of not spinning green?

P(green) + P(not green) = 1

P(not green) = 1 − P(green) = 1 − 0.2 = 0.8

Listing All Outcomes

A sample space diagram shows all the possible outcomes.

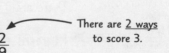
Try to order your lists — here there are 3 choices for the first digit, then the other 2 digits can swap round.

1) It can just be a simple list...

> E.g. Find all the 3-digit numbers that include the digits 1, 2 and 3.   123, 132, 213, 231, 321, 312

2) Or you can draw a two-way table if there are two activities going on (e.g. two coins being tossed, or a dice being thrown and a spinner being spun).

EXAMPLE: The spinner on the right is spun twice, and the scores added together.

a) Complete this sample space diagram showing all the possible outcomes.

+	1	2	3
1	2	3	4
2	3	4	5
3	4	5	6

There are 9 possible outcomes here — even though some of the actual scores are repeated.

b) Find the probability of spinning a total of 3.

$$P(\text{total of 3}) = \frac{\text{ways to score 3}}{\text{total number of possible outcomes}} = \frac{2}{9}$$

There are 2 ways to score 3.

c) Find the probability of spinning a total of 4 or more.

$$P(\text{total of 4 or more}) = \frac{\text{ways to score 4 or more}}{\text{total number of possible outcomes}} = \frac{6}{9} = \frac{2}{3}$$

There are 6 ways to score either 4, 5 or 6.

Sample space diagrams — they're out of this world...

What is the probability of you acing your exam? A lot higher once you've tackled this question:

Q1 Two fair dice are thrown, and their scores added together. By drawing a sample space diagram,

a) find the probability of throwing a total of 7, [3 marks]

b) find the probability of throwing any total except 7. [1 mark]

Probability Experiments

The formula on page 107 only works when the outcomes are equally likely. If they're <u>not equally likely</u>, you can use the results from experiments to <u>estimate</u> the probability of each outcome.

Do the Experiment Again and Again...

You need to do an experiment <u>over and over again</u> and count how many times each outcome happens (its <u>frequency</u>). Then you can calculate the <u>relative frequency</u> using this formula:

$$\text{Relative frequency} = \frac{\text{Frequency}}{\text{Number of times you tried the experiment}}$$

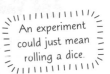

An experiment could just mean rolling a dice.

> You can use the <u>relative frequency</u> of a result as an <u>estimate</u> of its <u>probability</u>.

EXAMPLE: The spinner on the right was spun 100 times and the results recorded. Estimate the probability of getting each of the scores.

Score	1	2	3	4	5	6
Frequency	3	14	41	20	18	4

<u>Divide</u> each of the frequencies by 100 to find the <u>relative frequencies</u>.

Score	1	2	3	4	5	6
Relative Frequency	$\frac{3}{100}$ = 0.03	$\frac{14}{100}$ = 0.14	$\frac{41}{100}$ = 0.41	$\frac{20}{100}$ = 0.2	$\frac{18}{100}$ = 0.18	$\frac{4}{100}$ = 0.04

The <u>MORE TIMES</u> you do the experiment, the <u>MORE ACCURATE</u> your estimate of the probability should be.

E.g. if you spun the above spinner <u>1000 times</u>, you'd get a <u>better</u> estimate of the probability for each score.

Fair or Biased?

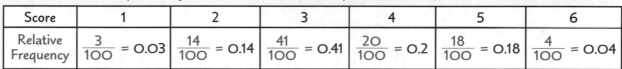

'Fair' means all the outcomes are <u>equally likely</u>. If something is unfair, it's called <u>biased</u>.

1) If the dice/spinner/coin/etc. is <u>fair</u>, then the relative frequencies of the results should <u>roughly match</u> the probabilities you'd get using the formula on p.107.

2) If the relative frequencies are <u>far away</u> from those probabilities, you can say it's probably <u>biased</u>.

EXAMPLE: Do the above results suggest that the spinner is biased?
Yes, because the relative frequency of 3 is much higher than you'd expect, while the relative frequencies of 1 and 6 are much lower.

For a <u>fair</u> 6-sided spinner, you'd expect all the relative frequencies to be about 1 ÷ 6 = 0.17(ish).

This topic is tough — make sure you revise it relatively frequently...

Remember that relative frequency can only be used to <u>estimate</u> the probability of a result. You can increase the <u>accuracy</u> of your estimate by increasing the number of times you do the experiment.

Q1 This table shows how many times Jenny and Sandro got a free biscuit on their visits to a coffee shop.

	Jenny	Sandro
Visits to coffee shop	20	150
Got a free biscuit	13	117

a) Based on Jenny's results, estimate the probability of getting a free biscuit at the shop. [2 marks]

b) Whose results will give a better estimate of the probability? Explain your answer. [1 mark]

Probability Experiments

OK, I'll admit it, probability experiments aren't as fun as science experiments but they are <u>useful</u>.

Record Results in Frequency Trees

When an experiment has two or more steps, you can record the results using a <u>frequency tree</u>.

EXAMPLE: 120 GCSE maths students were asked if they would go on to do A-level maths.
- 45 of them said they would go on to do A-level maths.
- 30 of the students who said they would do A-level maths actually did.
- 9 of the students who said they wouldn't do A-level maths actually did.

a) Complete the frequency tree below.

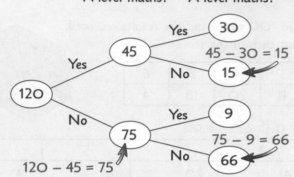

Will they take A-level maths?   Did they take A-level maths?

Yes — 30
45
45 – 30 = 15
No — 15

120
No — 75
120 – 45 = 75
Yes — 9
75 – 9 = 66
No — 66

b) A student who said they wouldn't do A-level maths is chosen at random. What is the probability that they <u>did</u> do A-level maths?

<u>9</u> out of the <u>75 students</u> who said they wouldn't do A-level maths actually did.

So the probability is $\frac{9}{75}$ = 0.12

Use Probability to Find an "Expected Frequency"

1) You can <u>estimate</u> how many times you'd <u>expect</u> something to happen if you do an experiment <u>n times</u>.

2) This <u>expected frequency</u> is based on the <u>probability</u> of the result happening.

Expected frequency of a result = probability × number of trials

A trial is a single experiment

EXAMPLE: A person spins the fair spinner on the right 200 times. Estimate how many times it will land on 5.

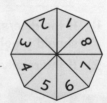

1) First calculate the probability of the spinner <u>landing on 5</u>.

$$P(\text{lands on 5}) = \frac{\text{ways to land on 5}}{\text{number of possible outcomes}} = \frac{1}{8}$$

2) Then <u>multiply</u> by <u>200</u> spins.

Expected number of 5's = P(lands on 5) × number of trials

$$= \frac{1}{8} \times 200 = 25 \text{ times}$$

If you don't know the probability of a result, fear not...
... you can estimate the probability using the <u>relative frequency</u> of the result in <u>past</u> experiments.

I expect you'll be looking back at this page quite frequently...

Expected frequencies are <u>estimates</u> for the <u>number of times</u> results will happen in a given number of trials. An expected frequency of 5 <u>doesn't mean</u> you expect it to happen <u>exactly</u> 5 times, just 'about 5 times'.

Q1 Using the frequency tree above, find the probability that a randomly chosen student said they were going to do A-level maths but didn't actually do it. [2 marks]

Q2 The spinner above is spun 300 times.
Estimate how many times it will land on an even number. [2 marks]

The AND / OR Rules

This page will show you how to find probabilities when <u>more than one</u> thing is happening at a time.

Combined Probability — Two or More Events

1) Always start by working out what different <u>SINGLE EVENTS</u> you're interested in.
2) Find the probability of <u>EACH</u> of these <u>SINGLE EVENTS</u>.
3) Apply the <u>AND/OR</u> rule.

And now for the rules. Say you have <u>two events</u> — call them A and B...

The AND Rule

This only works when the two events are <u>independent</u> — one event happening <u>does not affect</u> the chances of the other happening.

The probability of event A <u>AND</u> event B happening is equal to the probability of event A <u>MULTIPLIED BY</u> the probability of event B.

 Dave picks one ball at random from each of bags X and Y.
Find the probability that he picks a yellow ball from both bags.

1) The <u>single events</u> you're interested in are 'picks a yellow ball from bag X' and 'picks a yellow ball from bag Y'.

2) Find the <u>probabilities</u> of the events.   P(Dave picks a yellow ball from bag X) = $\frac{4}{10}$ = 0.4

P(Dave picks a yellow ball from bag Y) = $\frac{2}{8}$ = 0.25

3) Use the <u>AND rule</u>.   P(Dave picks a yellow ball from bag X <u>AND</u> bag Y) = 0.4 × 0.25 = 0.1

The OR Rule

This rule only works when the two events <u>can't both happen</u> at the same time.

The probability of <u>EITHER</u> event A <u>OR</u> event B happening is equal to the probability of event A <u>ADDED TO</u> the probability of event B.

 A spinner with red, blue, green and yellow sections is spun — the probability of it landing on each colour is shown in the table. Find the probability of spinning either red or green.

Colour	red	blue	yellow	green
Probability	0.25	0.3	0.35	0.1

1) The <u>single events</u> you're interested in are 'lands on red' and 'lands on green'.
2) Write down the <u>probabilities</u> of the events.   P(lands on red) = 0.25   P(lands on green) = 0.1
3) Use the <u>OR rule</u>.   P(Lands on <u>either</u> red <u>OR</u> green) = 0.25 + 0.1 = 0.35

Learn AND remember this — OR you're in trouble...

The way to remember this is that it's the wrong way round — you'd want AND to go with '+' but it doesn't. It's 'AND with ×' and 'OR with +'. Once you've got that, try this Exam Practice Question.

Q1   Shaun is a car salesman. The probability that he sells a car on a Monday is 0.8.
The probability that he sells a car on a Tuesday is 0.9.
What is the probability that he sells a car on both Monday and Tuesday?   [2 marks]

Q2   a) What is the probability of spinning blue OR yellow on the spinner above?   [2 marks]
b) What is the probability of spinning blue THEN green?   [2 marks]

Tree Diagrams

Tree diagrams can really help you work out probabilities when you have a <u>combination of events</u>.

Remember These Four Key Tree Diagram Facts

1) For branches which meet at a point, the probabilities <u>add up to 1</u>.

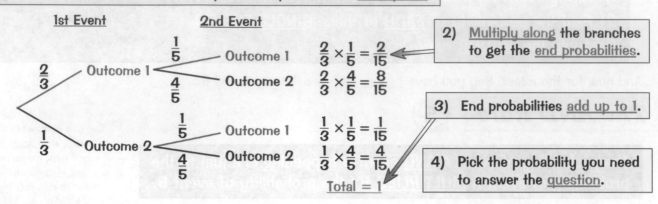

1st Event   2nd Event

$\frac{2}{3}$

Outcome 1

$\frac{1}{5}$ — Outcome 1 $\frac{2}{3} \times \frac{1}{5} = \frac{2}{15}$

$\frac{4}{5}$ — Outcome 2 $\frac{2}{3} \times \frac{4}{5} = \frac{8}{15}$

$\frac{1}{3}$

Outcome 2

$\frac{1}{5}$ — Outcome 1 $\frac{1}{3} \times \frac{1}{5} = \frac{1}{15}$

$\frac{4}{5}$ — Outcome 2 $\frac{1}{3} \times \frac{4}{5} = \frac{4}{15}$

Total = 1

2) <u>Multiply along</u> the branches to get the <u>end probabilities</u>.

3) End probabilities <u>add up to 1</u>.

4) Pick the probability you need to answer the <u>question</u>.

EXAMPLE: A box contains only red and green discs. A disc is taken at random from the box and replaced. A second disc is then taken. The tree diagram below shows the probabilities of picking each colour.

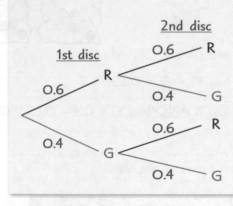

2nd disc

1st disc

0.6 — R

0.6 R

0.4 — G

0.4 G

0.6 — R

0.4 — G

a) What is the probability that both discs are red?

<u>Multiply</u> along the <u>branches</u> to find the probability you want:

P(both discs are red) = P(red, red) = 0.6 × 0.6 = 0.36

b) What is the probability that you pick a green disc then a red disc?

<u>Multiply</u> along the <u>branches</u> to find the probability you want:

P(green, red) = 0.4 × 0.6 = 0.24

Watch out for events that are affected by <u>what else has happened</u>
— you'll get <u>different probabilities</u> on different sets of branches.

EXAMPLE: Florence either walks or drives to work. The probability that she <u>walks</u> is <u>0.3</u>. If she <u>walks</u>, the probability that she is <u>late</u> is <u>0.8</u>. If she <u>drives</u>, the probability that she is <u>late</u> is <u>0.1</u>. Complete the tree diagram below.

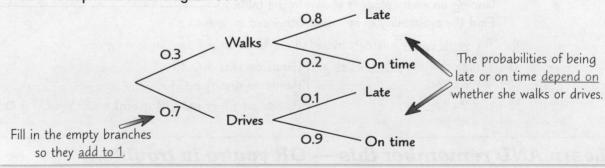

0.8 — Late

Walks

0.3

0.2 — On time

0.7

Drives

0.1 — Late

0.9 — On time

The probabilities of being late or on time <u>depend on</u> whether she walks or drives.

Fill in the empty branches so they <u>add to 1</u>.

Please don't make a bad tree-based joke. Oak-ay, just this once...

How convenient — answers growing on trees. Learn the routine, and then have a go at this...

Q1   Using the first tree diagram, find the probability of picking two green discs.   [2 marks]

Q2   Using the second tree diagram, find the probability that Florence drives to work and is late.   [2 marks]

Sets and Venn Diagrams

Venn diagrams are a way of displaying sets in intersecting circles — they're very pretty.

A Set is a Collection of Numbers or Objects

1) Sets are just collections of things — we call these 'things' elements.

2) Sets can be written in different ways but they'll always be in a pair of curly brackets {}. You can:

Each of these → • list the elements in the set, e.g. {2, 3, 5, 7}.

describes the → • give a description of the elements in the set, e.g. {prime numbers less than 10}.

same set. → • use formal notation, e.g. {x : x is a prime number less than 10}.

3) The symbol ∈ means 'is a member of'. So x ∈ A means 'x is a member of A'.

4) The universal set (ξ) is the group of things that the elements of the set are selected from.

Show Sets on Venn Diagrams

1) On a Venn diagram, each set is represented by a circle.
The universal set is everything inside the rectangle.

2) The diagram can show either the actual elements of each set, or the number of elements in each set.

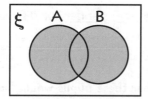

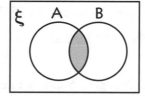

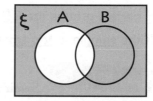

The union of sets A and B (written A ∪ B) contains all the elements in either set A or set B — it's everything inside the circles.

The intersection of sets A and B (written A ∩ B) contains all the elements in both set A and set B — it's where the circles overlap.

The complement of set A (written A') contains all members of the universal set that aren't in set A — it's everything outside circle A.

EXAMPLE: In a class of 30 pupils, 8 of them like mustard, 24 of them like ketchup and 5 of them like both mustard and ketchup.

a) Complete the Venn diagram below showing this information.

Start by filling in the overlap.

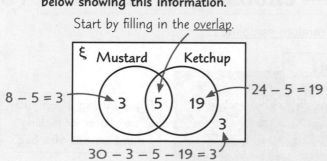

$8 - 5 = 3$

$24 - 5 = 19$

$30 - 3 - 5 - 19 = 3$

b) How many pupils like mustard or ketchup?

This is the number of pupils in the union of the two sets. $3 + 5 + 19 = 27$

c) What is the probability that a randomly selected pupil will like mustard and ketchup?

5 out of 30 pupils are in the intersection. $\frac{5}{30} = \frac{1}{6}$

This is P(M ∩ K).

The intersection of {Things I love} and {circles} = {Venn diagrams}...

Once you've got your head round the new words to learn, the exam questions aren't too bad.

Q1 50 birdwatchers were looking for pigeons and seagulls. 28 of them saw a pigeon, 15 of them saw both birds and 10 of them didn't see either bird. Show this information on a Venn diagram and use it to find the probability that a randomly selected birdwatcher saw a seagull. [4 marks]

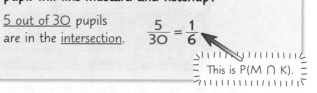

Sampling and Bias

Sampling is about using what you know about <u>smaller</u> groups to tell you about <u>bigger</u> groups. Simple, or is it...

Use a Sample to Find Out About a Population

1) For any statistical project, you need to find out about a <u>group</u> of people or things. E.g. all the pupils in a school, or all the trees in a forest. This <u>whole group</u> is called the <u>POPULATION</u>.

2) Often you <u>can't</u> collect information about <u>every member</u> of the population because there are <u>too many</u>. So you <u>select a smaller group</u> from the population, called a <u>SAMPLE</u>, instead.

3) It's really <u>important</u> that your <u>sample fairly represents</u> the <u>WHOLE</u> population. This allows you to <u>apply</u> any <u>conclusions</u> about your sample to the <u>whole population</u>.

> E.g. if you find that ¾ of the people in your <u>sample</u> like cheese, you can <u>estimate</u> that ¾ of the people in the <u>whole population</u> like cheese.

You Need to Spot Problems with Sampling Methods

A <u>BIASED</u> sample (or survey) is one that <u>doesn't properly represent</u> the <u>whole population</u>.

To <u>SPOT BIAS</u>, you need to <u>think about</u>:

> 1) <u>WHEN</u>, <u>WHERE</u> and <u>HOW</u> the sample is taken.
> 2) <u>HOW MANY</u> members are in it.

If certain groups are <u>left out</u> of the sample, there can be <u>BIAS</u> in things like <u>age</u>, <u>gender</u>, or different <u>interests</u>. If the <u>sample</u> is <u>too small</u>, it's also likely to be <u>biased</u>.

Bigger populations need bigger samples to represent them.

 **EXAMPLE:**

> Samir's school has 800 pupils. Samir is interested in whether these pupils would like to have more music lessons. For his sample he selects 5 members of the school orchestra to ask.
>
> Explain why the opinions Samir collects from his sample might not represent the whole school.
>
> Only members of the orchestra are included, so the opinions are likely to be biased in favour of more music lessons. And a sample of 5 is too small to represent the whole school.

If possible, the best way to <u>AVOID BIAS</u> is to select a <u>large</u> sample at <u>random</u> from the <u>whole population</u>.

Simple Random Sampling — choosing at Random

One way to get a <u>random</u> sample is to use '<u>simple random sampling</u>'.

> To <u>SELECT</u> a <u>SIMPLE RANDOM SAMPLE</u>...
> ❶ <u>Assign a number</u> to <u>every member</u> of the population.
> ❷ Create a <u>list</u> of <u>random numbers</u>. ◄──── E.g. by using a computer, calculator or picking numbers out of a bag.
> ❸ <u>Match</u> the random numbers to members of the population.

If you ask me, I love this page — but I'm biased...

Make sure you understand why samples should be representative and how to spot when they're not. Then you'll be ready to take on this Exam Practice Question.

Q1   Tina wants to find out how often people in the UK travel by train. She decides to ask 20 people waiting for trains at her local train station one morning. Comment on whether Tina can use the results of her survey to draw conclusions about the whole population. [2 marks]

Collecting Data

Data you <u>collect yourself</u> is called <u>primary</u> data. If you use data that <u>someone else has collected</u>, e.g. you get it from a website, it's called <u>secondary</u> data. You need to <u>record</u> primary data in a way that's <u>easy to analyse</u> and <u>suitable</u> for the <u>type</u> of data you've got.

There are Different Types of Data

QUALITATIVE DATA is <u>descriptive</u>. It uses <u>words</u>, not numbers.	E.g. <u>pets' names</u> — Smudge, Snowy, Dave, etc. <u>Favourite flavours of ice cream</u> — 'vanilla', 'chocolate', 'caramel-marshmallow-ripple', etc.
QUANTITATIVE DATA measures <u>quantities</u> using <u>numbers</u>.	E.g. <u>heights</u> of people, <u>times taken</u> to finish a race, <u>numbers of goals</u> scored in football matches, and so on.

There are two types of <u>quantitative</u> data.

<u>DISCRETE</u> DATA
1) It's <u>discrete</u> if the numbers can only take certain <u>exact</u> values.
2) E.g. the number of customers in a shop each day has to be a whole number — you can't have half a person.

<u>CONTINUOUS</u> DATA
1) If the numbers can take <u>any value</u> in a range, it's called <u>continuous</u> data.
2) E.g. heights and weights are continuous measurements.

You can Organise your Data into Classes

1) To record data in a <u>table</u>, you often need to <u>group</u> it into <u>classes</u> to make it more manageable. <u>Discrete</u> data classes should have '<u>gaps</u>' between them, e.g. '<u>0-1 goals</u>', '<u>2-3 goals</u>' (it jumps from 1 to 2 because there are no values in between). <u>Continuous</u> data classes should have <u>no 'gaps'</u>, so are often written using <u>inequalities</u> (see p.122).

2) Whatever the data you have, make sure <u>none of the classes overlap</u> and that they <u>cover all the possible values</u>.

When you <u>group</u> data you <u>lose</u> <u>some accuracy</u> because you don't know the exact values any more.

EXAMPLE: Jonty wants to find out about the ages (in whole years) of people who use his local library. Design a table he could use to collect his data.

Include <u>columns</u> for: the <u>data values</u>, '<u>Tally</u>' to count the data and '<u>Frequency</u>' to show the totals.

Use <u>non-overlapping</u> classes — with <u>gaps</u> because the data's <u>discrete</u>.

Include classes like '<u>...or over</u>', '<u>...or less</u>' or '<u>other</u>' to <u>cover all options</u> in a sensible number of classes.

Age (whole years)	Tally	Frequency
0-19		
20-39		
40-59		
60-79		
80 or over		

Questionnaires should be Designed Carefully

Another way to record data is to ask people to fill in a <u>questionnaire</u>. Your <u>questions</u> should be:

<u>Watch out</u> for <u>response boxes</u> that could be <u>interpreted</u> in <u>different</u> ways, that <u>overlap</u>, or that <u>don't allow</u> for <u>all</u> possible answers.

1) <u>Clear</u> and <u>easy to understand</u>
2) <u>Easy</u> to <u>answer</u>
3) <u>Fair</u> — not leading or biased

A question is '<u>leading</u>' if it guides you to picking a particular answer.

I won't tell you what type of data it is — I'm too discrete...

You need to know what type of data you've got so you can record and display it in a suitable way.

Q1 James asks some students how many times they went to the cinema in the last year. Say whether this data is discrete or continuous and design a table to record it in. [2 marks]

Mean, Median, Mode and Range

Mean, median, mode and range pop up all the time in statistics questions — make sure you know what they are.

MODE = MOST common

MEDIAN = MIDDLE value (when values are in order of size)

MEAN = TOTAL of items ÷ NUMBER of items

RANGE = Difference between highest and lowest

REMEMBER:

Mode = most (emphasise the 'mo' in each when you say them)

Median = mid (emphasise the m*d in each when you say them)

Mean is just the average, but it's mean 'cos you have to work it out.

The Golden Rule

There's one vital step for finding the median that lots of people forget:

Always REARRANGE the data in ASCENDING ORDER (and check you have the same number of entries!)

You must do this when finding the median, but it's also really useful for working out the mode too.

EXAMPLE: Find the median, mode, mean, and range of these numbers: 2, 5, 3, 2, 0, 1, 3, 3

① Rearrange the numbers into ascending order. 0, 1, 2, (2, 3) 3, 3, 5
The **MEDIAN** is the middle value.   ← 4 numbers either side →
When there are two middle numbers, the
median is halfway between the two.   Median = 2.5

> To find the position of the median of n values, you can use the formula (n + 1) ÷ 2. Here, (8 + 1) ÷ 2 = position 4.5 — that's halfway between the 4th and 5th values.

② MODE (or modal value) is the most common value = 3

③ MEAN = $\dfrac{\text{total of items}}{\text{number of items}}$ = $\dfrac{0 + 1 + 2 + 2 + 3 + 3 + 3 + 5}{8}$ = $\dfrac{19}{8}$ = 2.375

④ RANGE = difference between highest and lowest values = 5 − 0 = 5

A Trickier Example

EXAMPLE: The heights (to the nearest cm) of 8 penguins at a zoo are 41, 43, 44, 44, 47, 48, 50 and 51.
Two of the penguins are moved to a different zoo. If the mean height of the remaining penguins is 44.5 cm, find the heights of the two penguins that moved.

Mean = $\dfrac{\text{total height}}{\text{no. of penguins}}$

So total height = no. of penguins × mean

Total height of 8 penguins = 368 cm.
Total height of remaining 6 penguins = 6 × 44.5 = 267 cm.
Combined height of penguins that moved = 368 − 267 = 101 cm.
So the heights must be 50 cm and 51 cm.

My favourite range is the Alps...

Q1   Find the mean, median, mode and range for these test scores: 6, 15, 12, 12, 11.   [4 marks]

Q2   A set of 8 heights has a mean of 1.6 m. A new height of 1.5 m is added.
Explain whether the mean of all 9 heights will be higher or lower than 1.6 m.   [1 mark]

Simple Charts and Graphs

Pictograms and bar charts both show <u>frequencies</u>. (Remember... frequency = '<u>how many</u> of something'.)

Pictograms Show Frequencies Using Symbols

Every pictogram has a <u>key</u> telling you what one symbol represents.

> ### With pictograms, you <u>MUST</u> use the <u>KEY</u>.

EXAMPLE: This pictogram shows how many peaches were sold by a greengrocer on different days.

a) How many peaches were sold on Tuesday?

Each circle represents <u>4 peaches</u>.   2 × 4 = 8 peaches

b) How many peaches were sold on Wednesday?

<u>Three-quarters</u> of a circle = <u>3 peaches</u>.   (3 × 4) + 3 = 15 peaches

c) 43 peaches were sold altogether. Work out how many peaches were sold on Friday and show this information on the diagram.

1) Add up the peaches for <u>Mon-Thurs</u>.   4 + 8 + 15 + (4 + 2) = 33

2) <u>Subtract</u> this from the <u>total</u>.   Friday = 43 − 33 = 10

3) You need <u>2 whole circles</u> (= 8), <u>plus</u> another <u>half a circle</u> (= 2).

Key:
● represents 4 peaches

Monday	●
Tuesday	●●
Wednesday	●●●◕
Thursday	●◖
Friday	

Half a circle = 2 peaches.

| Friday | ●●◖ |

Bar Charts Show Frequencies Using Bars

1) <u>Frequencies</u> on bar charts are shown by the <u>heights</u> of the different bars.

2) <u>Dual bar charts</u> show two things at once — they're good for <u>comparing</u> different sets of data.

EXAMPLE: This dual bar chart shows the number of men and women visiting a coffee shop on different days.

a) How many men visited the coffee shop altogether?

Add up the numbers shown by the heights of the <u>purple bars</u>.   4 + 3 + 6 + 2 = 15 men

b) On which day did the most women visit the coffee shop?

Find the <u>tallest</u> yellow bar.   **Tuesday**

c) What fraction of the visitors on Wednesday were women? Give your answer in its simplest form.

There were 2 + 6 = 8 visitors on Wednesday — and <u>2</u> of them were women. $\frac{2}{8} = \frac{1}{4}$

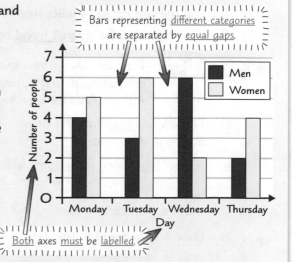

Bars representing <u>different categories</u> are separated by <u>equal gaps</u>.

<u>Both</u> axes <u>must</u> be <u>labelled</u>.

A sheep's favourite graph — the baaaa chart...

Q1   This pictogram shows the different types of CDs Javier owns, but the key is missing. Javier owns 20 blues CDs.

a) How many jazz CDs does Javier own?   [2 marks]

b) He owns 5 opera CDs. Complete the pictogram.   [1 mark]

Rock	●
Blues	●●
Opera	
Jazz	●◖

Simple Charts and Graphs

Here are <u>two-way tables</u>, <u>stem and leaf diagrams</u> and <u>line graphs</u>. Make sure you can draw and interpret them.

Two-Way Tables Show How Many in each Category

EXAMPLE: This table shows the number of cakes and pies a bakery sold on Friday and Saturday.

a) How many pies were sold on Saturday?
Read across to 'Pies' and down to 'Saturday'.   14 pies

b) How many items were sold in total on Friday?
<u>Add</u> the number of <u>cakes</u> for
<u>Friday</u> to the number of <u>pies</u>.   12 + 10 = 22

	Cakes	Pies	Total
Friday	12	10	
Saturday	4	14	18
Total	16	24	40

Or you could <u>subtract</u> the <u>total</u> for Saturday from the overall total: <u>40 − 18 = 22</u>.

Stem and Leaf Diagrams put data in Order

An <u>ordered stem and leaf diagram</u> shows a set of data in <u>order of size</u>.
This makes it <u>easy</u> to find things like the <u>median</u> and <u>range</u> (see p.116).

EXAMPLE: This stem and leaf diagram shows the ages of some school teachers.

a) How old is the oldest teacher?
Use the <u>key</u> to help you read off the diagram.   6 | 3 = 63 years old

b) What is the median age?
The <u>median</u> is the <u>middle</u> value.   There are 11 values, so the median is the 6th value.
Find its <u>position</u>, then read off the value.   So median age is 4 | 8 = 48 years

```
3 | 3 5
4 | 0 5 7 8
5 | 1 4 9
6 | 1 3
Key: 5|4 = 54 years
```

Line Graphs can show Time Series

1) A <u>time series</u> is when you measure the <u>same thing</u> at <u>different times</u>. A <u>line graph</u> of the data has 'time' along the bottom and the thing being measured down the side.

2) A <u>basic pattern</u> often repeats itself — it's called <u>seasonality</u> (but it doesn't have to match the seasons).

3) You can also see the <u>overall trend</u> by looking at the <u>peaks and troughs</u>.

EXAMPLE: The table shows how much Jamie spent on heating during Spring/Summer and Autumn/Winter over 4 years.

6-month period	Spr / Sum	Aut / Win	Spr / Sum	Aut / Win	Spr / Sum	Aut / Win	Spr / Sum	Aut / Win
Amount spent (£)	250	350	300	375	290	400	300	425

a) Draw a line graph of this data on the grid opposite.

Put 'Time' along the <u>bottom</u> and 'Amount spent' down the <u>side</u>.

Label your <u>axes</u> at <u>equal</u> intervals.

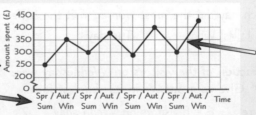

<u>Plot</u> the <u>points</u> and <u>join</u> them up with <u>straight</u> lines.
The pattern repeats itself <u>every 2 points</u>.

b) Describe the trend in the data.
Look at the <u>trend</u> in the <u>peaks</u>.   The data shows an upward trend in the amount Jamie spent.

I've seen a few programmes about herbs recently — a thyme series...

Q1 This data shows how many times Khalid goes rock-climbing in different quarters over 2 years.
a) Draw a line graph to show this data.   [2 marks]
b) In which quarter, each year, does Khalid go rock climbing most often?   [1 mark]

Quarter	1	2	3	4	1	2	3	4
Climbing	2	4	10	6	1	4	11	7

Pie Charts

Unlike other charts, <u>pie charts DON'T tell you numbers</u> of things, they show the <u>proportion in each category</u>. Remember that. And here's another thing to remember... the <u>Golden Pie Chart Rule</u>...

The TOTAL of Everything = 360°

1) Fraction of the Total = Angle ÷ 360°

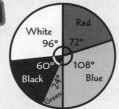

This pie chart shows the colour of all the cars sold by a dealer. What fraction of the cars were red?

$$\text{Fraction of red cars} = \frac{\text{angle of red cars}}{\text{angle of everything}} = \frac{72°}{360°} = \frac{1}{5}$$

2) Find a Multiplier to Calculate Your Angles

EXAMPLE: Draw a pie chart to show this information about the types of animal in a petting zoo.

Animal	Geese	Hamsters	Guinea pigs	Rabbits	Ducks
Number	12	20	17	15	26

1) Find the <u>total</u> by <u>adding</u>. 12 + 20 + 17 + 15 + 26 = 90

2) 'Everything = 360°' — so find the <u>multiplier</u> that turns your total into 360°.   Multiplier = 360 ÷ 90 = 4

3) <u>Multiply every number</u> by 4 to get the <u>angle</u> for each sector.

Angle	12 × 4 = 48°	20 × 4 = 80°	17 × 4 = 68°	15 × 4 = 60°	26 × 4 = 104°

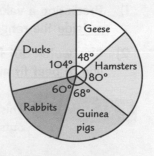

4) Draw your pie chart accurately using a <u>protractor</u>.

3) Find How Many by Using the Angle for 1 Thing

EXAMPLE: The pie chart on the right shows information about the types of animals liked most by different students. There were 90 students altogether.

a) Work out the number of students who liked dogs most.

1) 'Everything = 360°', so... ⟶ 90 students = 360°
2) <u>Divide by 90</u> to find... ⟶ 1 student = 4°
3) <u>Divide</u> the <u>angle for dogs</u> by the <u>angle for 1 student</u> to get: ⟶ 160° ÷ 4° = 40 — 40 students liked dogs most

b) The pie chart on the left shows information about the types of animals liked most by a different group of students. Dave says, "This means that 40 students in this group like dogs most." Explain why Dave is not correct.

We don't know how many students in total the pie chart represents, so we can't work out how many students liked dogs most.

I like my pie charts with gravy and mushy peas...

Pie chart questions need a lot of practice. Make a start with this...

Q1 Draw an accurate pie chart to show the information about Rahul's DVD collection given in this bar chart.   [4 marks]

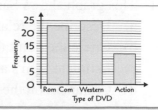

Scatter Graphs

A <u>scatter graph</u> tells you <u>how closely</u> two things are <u>related</u> — the fancy word is <u>CORRELATION</u>.

Scatter Graphs Show Correlation

1) If you can draw a <u>line of best fit</u> pretty close to <u>most</u> of your data points, the two things are <u>correlated</u>.
   If the points are <u>randomly scattered</u>, and you <u>can't draw</u> a line of best fit, then there's <u>no correlation</u>.

2) <u>Strong correlation</u> is when your points make a <u>fairly straight line</u> — the two things are <u>closely related</u>.
   <u>Weak correlation</u> is when your points <u>don't line up</u> so nicely, but you can still draw a line of best fit.

3) If the points form a line sloping <u>uphill</u> from left to right, then there is <u>positive correlation</u>.
   If the line slopes <u>downhill</u> from left to right, then there is <u>negative correlation</u>.

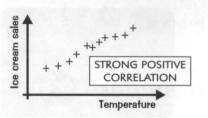

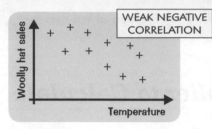

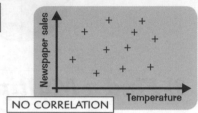

Use a Line of Best Fit to Make Predictions

1) Predicting a value <u>within the range</u> of data you have should be <u>fairly reliable</u>. But if you extend your line <u>outside</u> the range of data your prediction might be <u>unreliable</u>, because the <u>pattern might not continue</u>.

2) Also watch out for <u>outliers</u> — data points that <u>don't fit the general pattern</u>. Outliers can <u>drag</u> your <u>line of best fit</u> away from the other values, so it's best to <u>ignore</u> them when you're drawing the line.

EXAMPLE: This graph shows the number of zoo visitors plotted against the outside temperature for several Sundays.

Draw a <u>line of best fit</u> to <u>estimate</u> the <u>number of visitors</u> when the temperature is <u>15 °C</u>.
2250 should be a <u>reliable</u> estimate.

It doesn't make sense to extend the line below zero visitors.

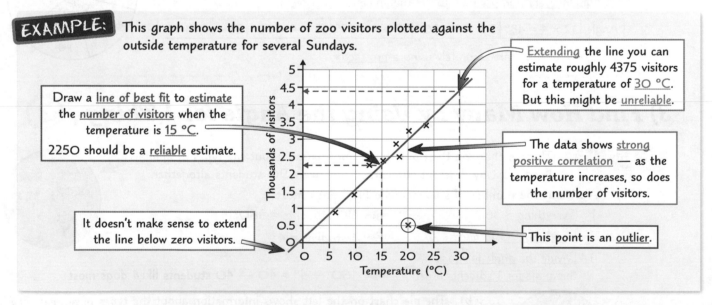

Extending the line you can estimate roughly 4375 visitors for a temperature of <u>30 °C</u>. But this might be <u>unreliable</u>.

The data shows <u>strong positive correlation</u> — as the temperature increases, so does the number of visitors.

This point is an <u>outlier</u>.

<u>BE CAREFUL</u> with <u>correlation</u> — if two things are correlated it <u>doesn't mean</u> that one causes the other. There could be a third factor affecting both, or it could just be a coincidence.

Relax and take a trip down Correlation Street...

Q1 This graph shows Sam's average speed on runs of different lengths.
   a) Describe the relationship between length of run and average speed. [1 mark]
   b) Circle the point that doesn't follow the trend. [1 mark]
   c) Estimate Sam's average speed for an 8-mile run. [1 mark]
   d) Comment on the reliability of your estimate in part c). [1 mark]

Frequency Tables — Finding Averages

The word <u>FREQUENCY</u> means <u>HOW MANY</u>, so a frequency table is just a '<u>How many in each category</u>' table. You saw how to find <u>averages and range</u> on p.116 — it's the same ideas here, but with the data in a table.

Find Averages from Frequency Tables

1) The <u>MODE</u> is just the <u>CATEGORY</u> with the <u>MOST ENTRIES</u>.

2) The <u>RANGE</u> is found from the <u>extremes of the first column</u>.

3) The <u>MEDIAN</u> is the <u>CATEGORY</u> of the <u>middle value</u>.

4) To find the <u>MEAN</u>, you have to <u>WORK OUT A THIRD COLUMN</u> yourself.

The <u>MEAN</u> is then: **3rd Column Total ÷ 2nd Column Total**

Categories   How many

Number of cats	Frequency	
0	17	
1	22	
2	15	
3	7	

Mysterious 3rd column...

EXAMPLE: Some people were asked how many sisters they have. The table opposite shows the results.

Find the mode, the range, the mean and the median of the data.

Number of sisters	Frequency
0	7
1	15
2	12
3	8
4	4
5	0

1 The <u>MODE</u> is the <u>category</u> with the <u>most entries</u> — i.e. the one with the <u>highest frequency</u>:

The highest frequency is 15 for '1 sister', so <u>MODE</u> = 1

2 The <u>RANGE</u> is the <u>difference</u> between the highest and lowest numbers of sisters — that's 4 sisters (no one has 5 sisters) and no sisters, so:

<u>RANGE</u> = 4 − 0 = 4

3 To find the <u>MEAN</u>, <u>add a 3rd column</u> to the table showing '<u>number of sisters × frequency</u>'. <u>Add up</u> these values to find the <u>total number of sisters</u> of all the people asked.

Number of sisters	Frequency	No. of sisters × Frequency
0	7	0
1	15	15
2	12	24
3	8	24
4	4	16
5	0	0
Total	46	79

3rd column total

$$\text{MEAN} = \frac{\text{total number of sisters}}{\text{total number of people asked}} = \frac{79}{46} = 1.72 \text{ (3 s.f.)}$$

2nd column total

4 The <u>MEDIAN</u> is the <u>category</u> of the <u>middle</u> value. Work out its <u>position</u>, then <u>count through</u> the 2nd column to find it.

It helps to imagine the data set out in an ordered list:
0000000111111111111111222222222222333333334444
median

The median is in position (n + 1) ÷ 2 = (46 + 1) ÷ 2 = 23.5 — halfway between the 23rd and 24th values. There are a total of (7 + 15) = 22 values in the first two categories, and another 12 in the third category takes you to 34. So the 23rd and 24th values must both be in the category '2 sisters', which means the <u>MEDIAN</u> is 2.

My table has 5 columns, 6 rows and 4 legs...

Learn the four key points about averages, then try this fella.

Q1 50 people were asked how many times a week they play sport. The table opposite shows the results.

    a) Find the median.   [2 marks]

    b) Calculate the mean.   [3 marks]

No. of times sport played	Frequency
0	8
1	15
2	17
3	6
4	4
5 or more	0

Grouped Frequency Tables

Grouped frequency tables are like ordinary frequency tables, but they group the data into classes.

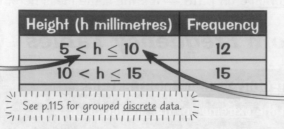

NO GAPS between classes for **CONTINUOUS** data.

Use <u>inequality symbols</u> to cover all possible values.

Height (h millimetres)	Frequency
5 < h ≤ 10	12
10 < h ≤ 15	15

See p.115 for grouped <u>discrete</u> data.

To find MID-INTERVAL VALUES:
- Add together the <u>end values</u> of the <u>class</u> and <u>divide by 2</u>.
- E.g. (5 + 10) ÷ 2 = <u>7.5</u>

Find Averages from Grouped Frequency Tables   (5)

Unlike with ordinary frequency tables, you <u>don't know the actual data values</u>, only the <u>classes</u> they're in. So you have to **ESTIMATE THE MEAN**, rather than calculate it exactly. Again, you do this by <u>adding columns</u>:

1) Add a <u>3RD COLUMN</u> and enter the <u>MID-INTERVAL VALUE</u> for each class.

2) Add a <u>4TH COLUMN</u> to show '<u>FREQUENCY × MID-INTERVAL VALUE</u>' for each class.

You'll be asked to find the <u>MODAL CLASS</u> and the <u>CLASS CONTAINING THE MEDIAN</u>, not exact values. And the <u>RANGE</u> can only be estimated too — using the class boundaries.

This table shows information about the weights, in kilograms, of 60 school children.

a) Write down the <u>modal class</u>.
b) Write down the <u>class containing the median</u>.
c) Calculate an <u>estimate for the mean weight</u>.
d) Estimate the <u>range of weights</u>.

Weight (w kg)	Frequency
30 < w ≤ 40	8
40 < w ≤ 50	16
50 < w ≤ 60	18
60 < w ≤ 70	12
70 < w ≤ 80	6

a) The <u>modal class</u> is the one with the <u>highest frequency</u>.

Modal class is 50 < w ≤ 60

b) Work out the <u>position</u> of the <u>median</u>, then <u>count through</u> the <u>2nd column</u>.

The median is in position (n + 1) ÷ 2 = (60 + 1) ÷ 2 = 30.5, halfway between the 30th and 31st values. Both these values are in the third class, so the class containing the median is 50 < w ≤ 60.

c) Add extra columns for '<u>mid-interval value</u>' and '<u>frequency × mid-interval value</u>'. Add up the values in the 4th column to estimate the <u>total weight</u> of the 60 children.

Weight (w kg)	Frequency	Mid-interval value	Frequency × mid-interval value
30 < w ≤ 40	8	35	280
40 < w ≤ 50	16	45	720
50 < w ≤ 60	18	55	990
60 < w ≤ 70	12	65	780
70 < w ≤ 80	6	75	450
Total	60	—	3220

Mean ≈ $\frac{\text{total weight}}{\text{number of children}}$ ← 4th column total / 2nd column total

$= \frac{3220}{60} = 53.7$ kg (3 s.f.)

d) Find the <u>difference</u> between the <u>highest</u> and <u>lowest</u> class <u>boundaries</u>.

Estimated range = 80 − 30 = 50 kg

This is the <u>largest possible</u> range. The actual range is likely to be smaller, but you can't tell with grouped data.

Mid-interval value — cheap ice creams...   (5)

Q1 a) Find the modal class. [1 mark]
b) Estimate the mean of this data.
Give your answer to 3 significant figures.

Length (l cm)	15.5 ≤ l < 16.5	16.5 ≤ l < 17.5	17.5 ≤ l < 18.5	18.5 ≤ l < 19.5
Frequency	12	18	23	8

[4 marks]

Interpreting Data

This page is about <u>getting information</u> from data and <u>recognising</u> when it might be <u>misleading</u>.

You can Find Averages from Diagrams

EXAMPLE: This vertical line graph shows information on the number of pairs of penguin slippers a shop sells each day for 50 consecutive days.
Calculate the mean number of pairs sold each day.

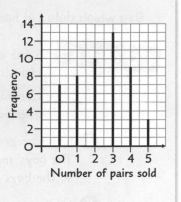

Fill in a <u>frequency table</u> and add a third column to find the total number of pairs sold — see p.121.

$$\text{Mean} = \frac{\text{total number of pairs sold}}{\text{total number of days}}$$

$$= \frac{118}{50} = 2.36$$

Number of pairs	Frequency	No. of pairs × Frequency
0	7	0
1	8	8
2	10	20
3	13	39
4	9	36
5	3	15
Total	50	118

Watch Out for Misleading Diagrams

At first glance, a diagram might look perfectly fine. But at second glance, well, not so fine...

EXAMPLE: This bar chart shows the numbers of dogs of different breeds at a rescue centre.
  a) Write down <u>three</u> things that are wrong with the bar chart.
  1) The 'number of dogs' axis doesn't start at zero.
  2) The 'number of dogs' axis has inconsistent numbering.
  3) The 'breed of dog' axis has no label.

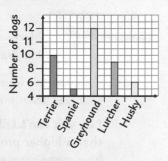

  b) The 'Husky' bar is twice as high as the 'Spaniel' bar.
  Explain why these bar heights could be misleading in the context of this data.
  The bar heights suggest that there are twice as many Huskies as Spaniels.
  But reading the scale, there are 6 Huskies and 5 Spaniels.

Be Careful with Measures of Average and Range

<u>Outliers</u> are data values that <u>don't fit</u> the <u>general pattern</u> — they're a long way from the rest of the data.
Outliers can have a <u>big effect</u> on the <u>mean</u> or <u>range</u> of a data set, so you get a <u>misleading</u> value.

EXAMPLE: The data below shows the number of songs Fred downloads each week for ten weeks.

0, 1, 3, 3, 5, 6, 7, 8, 8, 20

See p.116 for averages and range.

  a) Fred works out that the range of his data is 20. Comment on this value as a measure of the spread.
  A range of 20 isn't a true reflection of the spread of the whole data set, because most of the data is much closer together. The highest value of 20 has a big effect on increasing the range.
  b) Explain why the mode <u>isn't</u> a helpful measure of average for this data.
  The data has two modes, 3 and 8, so this doesn't give you a good idea of the average value.

Don't let data lead you down the garden path...

We should find out more about those penguin slippers. Use the data above to answer the following:
Q1 a) What is the modal number of pairs of penguin slippers sold? [1 mark]
  b) Use the data to estimate the probability that the shop will sell two pairs of penguin slippers on any given day. Comment on the reliability of your estimate. [3 marks]

Section Seven — Probability and Statistics

Comparing Data Sets

You can <u>compare</u> data sets using <u>averages</u> and <u>range</u>, or by <u>drawing suitable diagrams</u>.

Compare Data Sets Using Averages and Range

Say which data set has the <u>higher/lower</u> value and what that means in the <u>context of the data</u>.

EXAMPLE: Some children take part in a 'guess the weight of the baby hippo' competition. Here is some information about the weights they guess.

Compare the distributions of the weights guessed by the boys and the girls.

Boys:	Girls:
Mean = 40 kg	Mean = 34 kg
Median = 43 kg	Median = 33 kg
Range = 42 kg	Range = 30 kg

1 Compare <u>averages</u>:
The boys' mean and median values are higher than the girls', so the boys generally guessed heavier weights.

2 Compare <u>ranges</u>:
The boys' guesses have a bigger range, so the weights guessed by the boys show more variation.

Compare Data Sets Using Diagrams

The <u>type</u> of diagram you should use depends on <u>what you want to show</u>.

EXAMPLE: Harry carried out a survey into whether or not people like olives. He draws these pie charts to show his results.

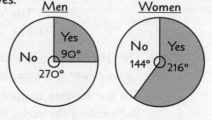

a) Can you tell from the pie charts whether more women said 'yes' than men? Explain your answer.

No, you can't tell whether more women said 'yes'. You can see that a higher proportion of women said 'yes' but you don't know how many men and women the pie charts represent.

b) Harry surveyed 20 men and 20 women. Draw a suitable diagram to compare the numbers of men and women giving each answer.

A <u>dual bar chart</u> is suitable — it shows the <u>numbers</u> of men and women <u>side by side</u>.

Use the pie charts to work out the <u>frequency</u> of each answer. E.g. find the fraction of the total, then multiply by 20.

Men: 'Yes' = $\frac{90}{360} \times 20 = 5$,   'No' = $\frac{270}{360} \times 20 = 15$

Women: 'Yes' = $\frac{216}{360} \times 20 = 12$,   'No' = $\frac{144}{360} \times 20 = 8$

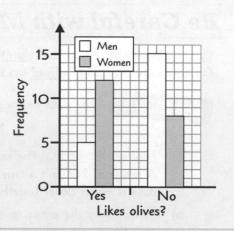

A pie isn't suitable for all occasions — hard to believe, I know...

You might need to work out the values of average and range (see p.116), before comparing data sets.

Q1 The data below shows how many football matches two supporters attended in each of the last nine years. Compare the distributions of the number of matches attended. [3 marks]

Hannah: 1, 5, 0, 7, 10, 8, 7, 4, 3
Joseph: 13, 17, 16, 20, 32, 18, 14, 25, 25

Revision Questions for Section Seven

Here's the inevitable list of straight-down-the-middle questions to test how much you know.

- Have a go at each question... but only tick it off when you can get it right without cheating.
- And when you think you could handle pretty much any statistics question, tick off the whole topic.

Probability (p107-110) ☑

1) I pick a random number between 1 and 50. Find the probability that my number is a multiple of 6. ☐

2) The probability of a spinner landing on red is 0.3. What is the probability that it doesn't land on red? ☐

3) I flip a fair coin 3 times.   a) Using H for heads and T for tails list all the possible outcomes.
   b) What is the probability of getting exactly one head? ☐

4) What are the formulas for: a) relative frequency?   b) expected frequency? ☐

5) 160 people took a 2-part test. 105 people passed the first part and of these,
   60 people passed the second part. 25 people didn't pass either test.
   a) Show this information on a frequency tree.   b) Find the relative frequency of each outcome.
   c) If 300 more people do the test, estimate how many of them would pass both parts. ☐

Harder Probability and Venn Diagrams (p111-113) ☑

6) The table shows the probabilities of a biased dice landing on each
   number. What is the probability of it landing on a 1 or a 4? ☐

Number	1	2	3	4	5	6
Probability	0.2	0.15	0.1	0.3	0.15	0.1

7) I have a standard pack of 52 playing cards. Use a tree diagram to find the probability of
   me picking two cards at random and getting no hearts if the first card is replaced. ☐

8) 100 people were asked whether they like tea or coffee. Half the people said they like coffee,
   34 people said they like tea, 20 people said they like both.
   a) Show this information on a Venn diagram.
   b) If one of the 100 people is randomly chosen, find the probability of them liking tea or coffee. ☐

Collecting Data and Finding Averages (p114-116) ☑

9) What is a sample and why does it need to be representative? ☐

Pet	Tally	Frequency

10) Is 'eye colour' descriptive, discrete or continuous data? ☐

11) Complete this frequency table for the data below. ⟶

   Cat, Cat, Dog, Dog, Dog, Rabbit, Fish, Cat, Rabbit, Rabbit, Dog, Dog, Cat, Cat, Dog, Rabbit, Cat, Fish, Cat, Cat ☐

12) Find the mode, median, mean and range of this data: 2, 8, 11, 15, 22, 24, 27, 30, 31, 31, 41 ☐

Graphs and Charts (p117-120) ☑

13) How do you find frequencies from a pictogram? ☐

Film rating	Terrible	Bad	OK	Good	Amazing
Students	40	30	40	45	25

14) The table opposite shows how some students rated a film.
   Draw a suitable diagram to show the number of students giving each rating. ☐

15) a) Draw a line graph to show the time series data in this table.
   b) Describe the repeating pattern in the data. ☐

Quarter	1	2	3	4	1	2	3	4
Sales (1000's)	1	1.5	1.7	3	0.7	0.9	1.2	2.2

16) Using the data in Q14, draw a suitable diagram to show the proportion of students giving each rating. ☐

17) Sketch graphs to show: a) weak positive correlation, b) strong negative correlation, c) no correlation ☐

Frequency Tables and Averages (p121-122) ☑

18) For this grouped frequency table showing the lengths of some pet alligators:
   a) find the modal class,
   b) find the class containing the median,
   c) estimate the mean.

Length (y, in m)	Frequency
$1.4 \leq y < 1.5$	4
$1.5 \leq y < 1.6$	8
$1.6 \leq y < 1.7$	5
$1.7 \leq y < 1.8$	2

☐

Interpreting and Comparing Data Sets (p123-124) ☑

19) Explain the effect that outliers can have on the mean and range of data. ☐

20) These pie charts show the results of a survey on the colour of people's cars.
   Compare the popularity of each colour of car amongst men and women. ☐

Men / Women

Answers

Get the full versions of these answers online
Step-by-step worked solutions to these questions, with a full mark scheme, are included as a printable PDF with your free Online Edition — you'll find more info about how to get hold of this at the front of this book.

Section One

Page 2 — Types of Number and BODMAS
Q1   55

Page 3 — Wordy Real-Life Problems
Q1   19p or £0.19

Page 4 — Multiplying and Dividing by 10, 100, etc.
Q1 a) 1230   **b)** 0.00308   **c)** 12

Page 5 — Multiplying and Dividing Whole Numbers
Q1 a) 336   **b)** 616   **c)** 1664
Q2 a) 12   **b)** 12   **c)** 21
Q3   10 cm

Page 6 — Multiplying and Dividing with Decimals
Q1 a) 179.2   **b)** 6.12   **c)** 56.1
Q2   £17.78
Q3   £7.46
Q4 a) 56   **b)** 30   **c)** 705

Page 7 — Negative Numbers
Q1 a) –6 °C   **b)** –5 °C

Page 8 — Prime Numbers
Q1   61, 53, 47

Page 9 — Multiples, Factors and Prime Factors
Q1 a) 24   **b)** 6
Q2   60
Q3 a) $990 = 2 \times 3 \times 3 \times 5 \times 11$
           $= 2 \times 3^2 \times 5 \times 11$
    b) $160 = 2 \times 2 \times 2 \times 2 \times 2 \times 5$
           $= 2^5 \times 5$

Page 10 — LCM and HCF
Q1   84   **Q2**   12

Page 11 — LCM and HCF
Q1   28   **Q2**   88

Page 13 — Fractions without a Calculator
Q1 a) $\frac{55}{48}$ or $1\frac{7}{48}$ **b)** $\frac{15}{28}$
    c) $\frac{43}{27}$ or $1\frac{16}{27}$ **d)** $-\frac{43}{12} = -3\frac{7}{12}$
Q2   6

Page 14 — Fraction Problems
Q1 $\frac{13}{21}$

Page 15 — Fractions, Decimals and Percentages
Q1 a) 57%   **b)** $\frac{6}{25}$ **c)** 90%
Q2 a) $\frac{555}{1000} = \frac{111}{200}$ **b)** $0.1\dot{6}$

Page 16 — Rounding Numbers
Q1 a) 21.4   **b)** 0.06   **c)** 5.0
Q2   3.11

Page 17 — Rounding Numbers
Q1 a) 700   **b)** 15
    c) 169   **d)** 82 000
Q2   4.8

Page 18 — Estimating
Q1 a) E.g. 400
    b) E.g. 5
Q2   E.g. £40

Page 19 — Rounding Errors
Q1   137.5 g
Q2 a) $375 \leq x < 385$
    b) $0.455 \leq y < 0.465$

Page 20 — Powers
Q1 a) 43   **b)** 238.328   **c)** 10^4
Q2 a) $4^5 (= 1024)$ **b)** $7^3 (= 343)$
    c) q^8
Q3 a) 36   **b)** $\frac{1}{16}$

Page 21 — Roots
Q1 a) 14   **b)** 21   **c)** 3
Q2   1.2 cm
Q3   17.12422442

Page 23 — Standard Form
Q1 a) 432 000 000   **b)** 3.87×10^{-4}
Q2 1.9×10^{-3}
Q3 a) 3×10^3 **b)** 1.9×10^{10}

Revision Questions — Section One
Q1   A square number is a whole number multiplied by itself. The first ten are: 1, 4, 9, 16, 25, 36, 49, 64, 81 and 100.
Q2   0.1
Q3   £38
Q4 a) £120   **b)** £0.50 = 50p
Q5 a) 1377   **b)** 26
    c) 62.7   **d)** 0.35
Q6 a) –16   **b)** 7   **c)** 20
Q7   41, 43, 47, 53, 59

Q8   The multiples of a number are its times table.
    a) 10, 20, 30, 40, 50, 60
    b) 4, 8, 12, 16, 20, 24
Q9 a) $210 = 2 \times 3 \times 5 \times 7$
    b) $1050 = 2 \times 3 \times 5 \times 5 \times 7$
           $= 2 \times 3 \times 5^2 \times 7$
Q10 a) 14   **b)** 40
Q11 a) $\frac{25}{16}$ or $1\frac{9}{16}$ **b)** $\frac{44}{15}$ or $2\frac{14}{15}$
    c) $\frac{23}{8}$ or $2\frac{7}{8}$ **d)** $\frac{11}{21}$
Q12 a) 320   **b)** £60
Q13   Amy
Q14 a) i) $\frac{4}{100} = \frac{1}{25}$ **ii)** 4%
    b) i) $\frac{65}{100} = \frac{13}{20}$ **ii)** 0.65
Q15 a) Recurring decimals have a pattern of numbers which repeats forever.
    b) $0.\dot{2}$
Q16 a) 17.7   **b)** 6700
    c) 4 000 000
Q17 a) 100   **b)** 1400
Q18 a) $150 \leq x < 250$
    b) $24.6 \leq y < 24.7$
Q19 7^5
Q20 $\frac{1}{25}$
Q21 a) 11   **b)** 4   **c)** 56   **d)** 10^5
Q22 a) 421.875   **b)** 4.8
    c) 8   **d)** 11
Q23   1. The front number must always be between 1 and 10.
    2. The power of 10, n, is how far the decimal point moves.
    3. n is positive for big numbers, and negative for small numbers.
Q24 a) 3.56×10^9 **b)** 0.00000275
Q25 a) 2×10^3 **b)** 1.2×10^{12}

Section Two

Page 25 — Algebra — Simplifying
Q1 a) $13a$ **b)** $10b$
Q2 a) $3x + 8y$ **b)** $9 + 3\sqrt{5}$

Page 26 — Algebra — Multiplying and Dividing
Q1 a) $-60rs$ **b)** $21m - 14$
    c) $4p^2 + 8pq$
Q2 $5(x + 8) + 2(x - 12)$
      $= 5x + 40 + 2x - 24 = 7x + 16$

Answers

Page 27 — Multiplying Double Brackets

Q1 a) $x^2 + x - 30$ **b)** $2y^2 + 17y - 9$
Q2 a) $x^2 - 6x + 9$ **b)** $16y^2 + 40y + 25$

Page 28 — Factorising

Q1 $6(2x + 5)$
Q2 $3y(2 + 5y)$
Q3 $(x + 5)(x - 5)$
Q4 $(6x + 7y)(6x - 7y)$

Page 29 — Solving Equations

Q1 a) $x = 6$ **b)** $x = 14$
   c) $x = 3$ **d)** $x = 15$

Page 30 — Solving Equations

Q1 $x = 5$
Q2 $y = 7$

Page 31 — Expressions, Formulas and Functions

Q1 $v = 29$
Q2 $x = 11$

Page 32 — Formulas and Equations from Words

Q1   Ali = 13 tickets, Ben = 26 tickets, Joe = 34 tickets
Q2   3, 15 and 30

Page 33 — Formulas and Equations from Diagrams

Q1 $x = 16$

Page 34 — Rearranging Formulas

Q1 $v = 3(u + 2)$ or $v = 3u + 6$
Q2 $d = \dfrac{c}{6} + 2$

Page 35 — Sequences

Q1   Rule = multiply the previous term by 2; next 2 terms = 24, 48
Rule = add 3, add 6, add 9... next 2 terms = 21, 33

Page 36 — Sequences

Q1 a) $7n - 5$ **b)** 51
   c) No, as the solution to $7n - 5 = 63$ doesn't give an integer value of n.

Page 37 — Inequalities

Q1 $n = -1, 0, 1, 2, 3, 4$
Q2 a) $x < 6$ **b)** $x \geq 3$

Page 38 — Quadratic Equations

Q1 $(x + 5)(x - 3)$
Q2 $x = 4$ or $x = 5$

Page 39 — Simultaneous Equations

Q1 $x = 1, y = 2$
Q2 $x = 3, y = -1$

Page 40 — Proof

Q1 a) E.g. 25   **b)** E.g. 2 and 3

Revision Questions — Section Two

Q1 a) $3e$ **b)** $12f$
Q2 a) $7x - y$ **b)** $3a + 9$
Q3 a) m^3 **b)** $7pq$ **c)** $18xy$
Q4 a) $6x + 18$ **b)** $-9x + 12$
   c) $5x - x^2$
Q5 $6x$
Q6 a) $2x^2 - x - 10$
   b) $25y^2 + 20y + 4$
Q7   Putting in brackets (the opposite of multiplying out brackets).
Q8 a) $8(x + 3)$ **b)** $9x(2x + 3)$
   c) $(6x + 9y)(6x - 9y)$
Q9 a) $x = 7$ **b)** $x = 16$ **c)** $x = 3$
Q10 a) $x = 4$ **b)** $x = 2$ **c)** $x = 3$
Q11 $Q = 8$
Q12   14
Q13   37 marbles
Q14 $6x$ cm
Q15 $v = \dfrac{W - 5}{4}$
Q16 a) 31, rule is add 7
   b) 256, rule is multiply by 4
   c) 19, rule is add previous two terms.
Q17 $6n - 2$
Q18   Yes, it's the 5th term.
Q19 a) x is greater than minus seven.
   b) x is less than or equal to six.
Q20 $k = 1, 2, 3, 4, 5, 6, 7$
Q21 a) $x < 10$ **b)** $x \leq 7$
Q22 a) $(x + 2)(x + 8)$
   b) $(x + 1)(x - 7)$
Q23 $x = -6$ or $x = 3$
Q24 $x = 2, y = 5$
Q25   E.g. 19
Q26 $3(y + 2) + 2(y + 6)$
$= 3y + 6 + 2y + 12$
$= 5y + 18 = 5(y + 3) + 3$.
$5(y + 3)$ is a multiple of 5, so $5(y + 3) + 3$ is not a multiple of 5.

Section Three

Page 42 — Coordinates and Midpoints

Q1 a)
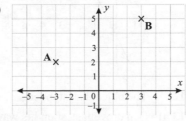
   b) Midpoint = (0, 3.5)

Page 43 — Straight-Line Graphs

Q1 a), b) and c)
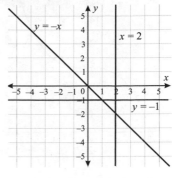

Page 44 — Drawing Straight-Line Graphs

Q1
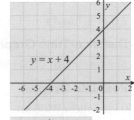

Q2
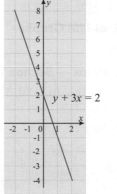

Page 45 — Straight-Line Graphs — Gradients

Q1 -5

Page 46 — Straight-Line Graphs — y = mx + c

Q1 -2

Page 47 — Using y = mx + c

Q1 a) $y = \dfrac{1}{2}x + 5$
   b) $y = \dfrac{1}{2}x + 10$

Page 48 — Quadratic Graphs

Q1 a)
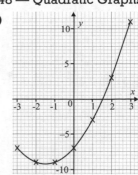
   b) $(-1.5, -9.25)$

Answers

Page 49 — Harder Graphs

Q1

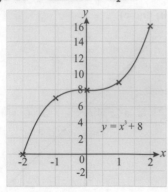

$y = x^3 + 8$

Page 50 — Solving Equations Using Graphs

Q1 $x = 6, y = 8$

Q2 $x = 2.6$ or 2.7 and $x = -1.2$ or -1.1

Page 51 — Distance-Time Graphs

Q1 a) 15 minutes   **b)** 12 km/h

Page 52 — Real-Life Graphs

Q1 9600 km (allow 9400 km to 9800 km)

Page 53 — Real-Life Graphs

Q1 Graph B

Revision Questions — Section Three

Q1 A(5, –3), B(4, 0), C(0, 3), D(–4, 5), E(–2, –3)

Q2 Midpoint = (2, 1.5)

Q3

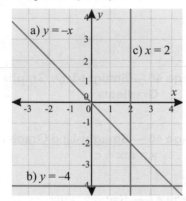

a) $y = -x$
c) $x = 2$
b) $y = -4$

Q4 E.g.

x	–2	0	2
y	6	–2	–10

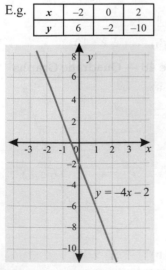

$y = -4x - 2$

Q5 a) 2   **b)** $y = x + 15$

Q6 $y = 2x - 6$

Q7 $y = x - 9$

Q8 They are both "bucket shaped" graphs. $y = x^2 - 8$ is like a "u" whereas $y = -x^2 + 2$ is like an "n" (or an upturned bucket).

Q9 a)

x	–3	–2	–1	0	1
y	0	–2	–2	0	4

b)

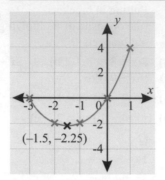

(–1.5, –2.25)

Q10 a) A graph with a "wiggle" in the middle. E.g.

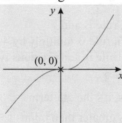

(0, 0)

b) A graph made up of two curves in opposite corners. The curves are symmetrical about the lines $y = x$ and $y = -x$.
E.g.

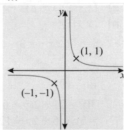

(1, 1)
(–1, –1)

Q11

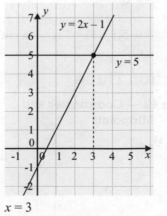

$y = 2x - 1$
$y = 5$

$x = 3$

Q12 The object has stopped.

Q13 a) Ben drove fastest on his way home.

b) 15 minutes

Q14 You would have to find the gradient, as the gradient = the rate of change.

Q15 a) 20 minutes
b) £20
c) 26 minutes
d) 67p — allow between 65p and 69p

Section Four

Page 55 — Ratios

Q1 a) $5:7$ **b)** $3:10$ **c)** $1:2.25$

Page 57 — Ratios

Q1 a) $\frac{2}{13}$ **b)** 33 litres

Q2 36 years old

Q3 9 cm

Q4 30 people

Page 58 — Direct Proportion Problems

Q1 a) 80p   **b)** 32

Q2 £67.50

Page 59 — Direct Proportion Problems

Q1 The 770 g bottle.

Q2 a) E.g.

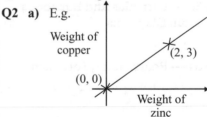

Weight of copper
(2, 3)
(0, 0)
Weight of zinc

b) The graph is a straight line through the origin.

Page 60 — Inverse Proportion Problems

Q1 1.5 hours

Q2 $m = 3.125$

Page 61 — Percentages

Q1 a) 108   **b)** 701.95

Q2 62%

Page 62 — Percentages

Q1 £3400

Q2 £129.80

Page 63 — Percentages

Q1 25%

Q2 £6.10

Page 64 — Percentages

Q1 56%

Q2 a) i) 2320   **ii)** 1972
b) 23.25%

Page 65 — Compound Growth and Decay

Q1 £3446.05

Page 66 — Unit Conversions

Q1 a) 975 cm
b) 32 feet 6 inches

Page 67 — Area and Volume Conversions

Q1 6 000 000 m²
Q2 40 000 mm³

Page 68 — Time Intervals

Q1 a) 2880 minutes
b) 4 minutes 25 seconds
Q2 £187.20

Page 70 — Speed, Density and Pressure

Q1 2800 N
Q2 a) 8 m/s **b)** 28.8 km/h
Q3 a) 3.125 g/cm³ **b)** 3125 kg/m³

Revision Questions — Section Four

Q1 a) 9 : 11 **b)** 3.5 : 1
Q2 80 blue scarves
Q3 $\frac{7}{2}$ or 3.5
Q4 a) $\frac{5}{25}$ or $\frac{1}{5}$ **b)** 384
Q5 51 ml olive oil, 1020 g tomatoes 25.5 g garlic powder, 204 g onions
Q6 960 flowers
Q7 See p.59
Q8 The 500 ml tin
Q9 18
Q10 a) 19 **b)** 114
c) 21.05% (2 d.p.) **d)** 475%
Q11 percentage change = (change ÷ original) × 100
Q12 35% decrease
Q13 17.6 m
Q14 2%
Q15 a) £117.13 (to the nearest penny)
b) 6 years
Q16 a) 5600 cm³ **b)** 240 cm
c) 336 hours **d)** 12 000 000 cm³
e) 12.8 cm² **f)** 2750 mm³
Q17 9.48 pm
Q18 67.2 km/h
Q19 12 500 cm³
Q20 11 m²

Section Five

Page 72 — Properties of 2D Shapes

Q1 a) E.g.

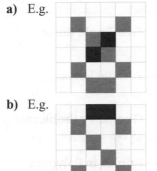

b) E.g.

Page 73 — Properties of 2D Shapes

Q1 Rhombus
Rotational symmetry of order 2

Page 74 — Congruent Shapes

Q1 $x = 6$ cm
$y = 44°$
$z = 55°$

Page 75 — Similar Shapes

Q1 BD = 10 cm

Page 76 — The Four Transformations

Q1

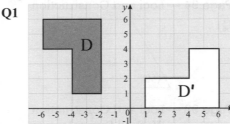

Page 77 — The Four Transformations

Q1

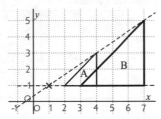

An enlargement of scale factor 2, centre (1, 1).

Page 78 — Perimeter and Area

Q1 75 cm² **Q2** $x = 10$

Page 79 — Perimeter and Area — Circles

Q1 a) i) 16π cm² **ii)** 16.76 cm (2 d.p.)
b) Area of sector B = $\frac{x}{360} \times \pi r^2$
$= \frac{90}{360} \times \pi \times 8^2$
$= 16\pi$ cm² = area of sector A

Page 80 — 3D Shapes

Q1 a) cuboid
b) (i) 6 **(ii)** 12 **(iii)** 8

Page 81 — 3D Shapes — Surface Area

Q1 392.7 cm² (1 d.p.)
Q2 7 cm

Page 82 — 3D Shapes — Volume

Q1 360 cm³

Page 83 — 3D Shapes — Volume

Q1 860π m³

Page 84 — 3D Shapes — Volume

Q1 Volume of sphere = $\frac{4}{3}\pi r^3$
$= \frac{4}{3} \times \pi \times 3^3$
$= 36\pi$ cm³
Volume of cylinder = $\pi r^2 h$
$= \pi \times 6^2 \times 10$
$= 360\pi$ cm³
$\frac{\text{Volume of cylinder}}{\text{Volume of sphere}} = \frac{360\pi}{36\pi}$
$= \frac{360}{36} = 10$

Q2 Volume of pyramid = 132 000 cm³
Time taken to fill = 1320 s
= 22 mins so yes, it takes longer than 20 mins to fill.

Page 85 — Projections

Q1 a) **b)**

c)

Revision Questions — Section Five

Q1 H: 2 lines of symmetry, rotational symmetry order 2
Z: 0 lines of symmetry, rotational symmetry order 2
T: 1 line of symmetry, rotational symmetry order 1
N: 0 lines of symmetry, rotational symmetry order 2
E: 1 line of symmetry, rotational symmetry order 1
✕: 4 lines of symmetry, rotational symmetry order 4
S: 0 lines of symmetry, rotational symmetry order 2
Q2 2 angles the same, 2 sides the same, 1 line of symmetry, no rotational symmetry.
Q3 2 lines of symmetry, rotational symmetry order 2

Answers

Q4 Congruent shapes are exactly the same size and same shape. Similar shapes are the same shape but different sizes.

Q5 a) D and G   **b)** C and F

Q6 $b = 89$, $y = 5$

Q7 a) Translation of $\begin{pmatrix} -2 \\ -4 \end{pmatrix}$.

    b) Reflection in $x = 0$ (the y-axis).

Q8

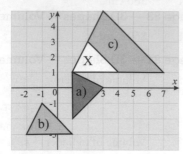

Q9 Area = $\frac{1}{2}(a + b) \times h$

Q10 36 cm^2

Q11 52 cm^2

Q12 Area = 153.94 cm^2 (2 d.p.)
Circumference = 43.98 cm (2 d.p.)

Q13 E.g.

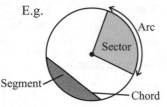

Q14 Area = 7.07 cm^2 (2 d.p.)
Perimeter = 10.71 cm (2 d.p.)

Q15 a) faces = 5, edges = 8, vertices = 5
    b) faces = 2, edges = 1, vertices = 1
    c) faces = 5, edges = 9, vertices = 6

Q16 150 cm^2

Q17 125.7 cm^2 (1 d.p.)

Q18 Volume = $\pi r^2 h$

Q19 360 cm^3

Q20 a) 113.10 cm^3 (2 d.p.)
    b) 4.5 s (1 d.p.)

Q21 Front: Side:

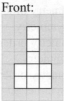

Plan:

Section Six

Page 87 — Angle Basics
Q1 a) Acute   **b)** 120°

Page 88 — Five Angle Rules
Q1 $x = 108°$

Page 89 — Parallel Lines
Q1 $x = 68°$

Page 90 — Geometry Problems
Q1 $x = 123°$

Page 91 — Angles in Polygons
Q1   144°   **Q2**   Pentagon

Page 92 — Triangle Construction
Q1

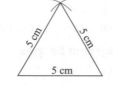

Not full size

Q2

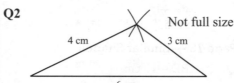

Not full size

Page 94 — Loci and Construction
Q1

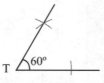

Page 95 — Loci and Construction — Worked Examples
Q1 Visitors can go anywhere in the shaded area.

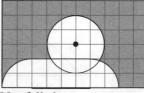

Not full size

Page 96 — Bearings
Q1   298°   **Q2**   030°

Page 97 — Maps and Scale Drawings
Q1   9 miles   **Q2**   4.5 cm

Page 98 — Maps and Scale Drawings
Q1 1 cm represents 200 m, so the woodland should be 1.25 cm by 1.5 cm, e.g.

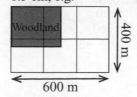

Q2

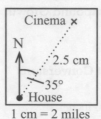

1 cm = 2 miles

Page 99 — Pythagoras' Theorem
Q1   10.3 m

Q2   3.8 m

Page 101 — Trigonometry — Examples
Q1 $y = 4.24$ cm

Q2 $x = 27.1°$

Page 102 — Trigonometry — Common Values
Q1 a) $\sqrt{3}$ cm   **b)** 3 m

Page 103 — Vectors — Theory
Q1 $\begin{pmatrix} 1 \\ 5 \end{pmatrix}$

Q2 $\mathbf{c} + \mathbf{d}$

Page 104 — Vectors — Examples
Q1 $\overrightarrow{EF} = 4\mathbf{p} + 4\mathbf{q}$

Revision Questions — Section Six
Q1 An obtuse angle

Q2 360°

Q3 a) 154°
    b) 112°
    c) 58°

Q4 140°

Q5 60°

Q6 1080°

Q7 162°

Q8

(Not full size)

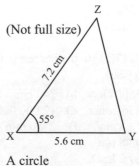

Q9 A circle

Q10

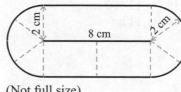

(Not full size)

Q11

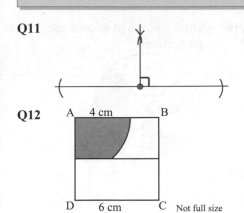

Q12

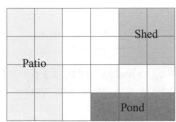

A   4 cm   B

D   6 cm   C   Not full size

Q13   295°

Q14   280°

Q15   26 km

Q16

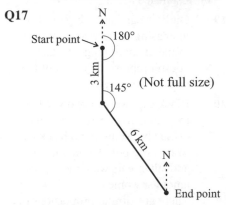

Shed

Patio

Pond

Q17

N

Start point   180°

3 km

145°   (Not full size)

6 km

N

End point

Q18   14.5 cm

Q19

O / S × H   A / C × H   O / T × A

Q20 $x = 33.4°$ (1 d.p.)

Q21 $x = 51.8°$ (1 d.p.)

Q22 $12\sqrt{3}$ cm

Q23 $\tan 45° + \sin 60° = 1 + \dfrac{\sqrt{3}}{2}$

$= \dfrac{2}{2} + \dfrac{\sqrt{3}}{2}$

$= \dfrac{2 + \sqrt{3}}{2}$

Q24 a) $\begin{pmatrix} -3 \\ -8 \end{pmatrix}$ **b)** $\begin{pmatrix} 20 \\ -10 \end{pmatrix}$

Q25 $2\mathbf{a} + 3\mathbf{b}$

Q26 $5\mathbf{a} - 7\mathbf{b}$

Q27 $-\mathbf{i} + \mathbf{j}$

Section Seven

Page 107 — Probability Basics

Q1 a) $\dfrac{3}{10}$ or 0.3

b) $\dfrac{6}{10} = \dfrac{3}{5}$ or 0.6

Q2

0.3   0.6

0   0.5   1

Page 108 — More Probability

Q1 a) $\dfrac{6}{36} = \dfrac{1}{6}$ **b)** $\dfrac{5}{6}$

Page 109 — Probability Experiments

Q1 a) $\dfrac{13}{20} = 0.65$

b) Sandro's results are based on more visits to the coffee shop, so his results will give a better estimate of the probability.

Page 110 — Probability Experiments

Q1 $\dfrac{15}{120} = 0.125$ **Q2** 150

Page 111 — The AND / OR Rules

Q1   0.72

Q2 a) 0.65   **b)** 0.03

Page 112 — Tree Diagrams

Q1   0.16

Q2   0.07

Page 113 — Sets and Venn Diagrams

Q1

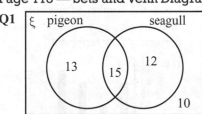

ξ   pigeon   seagull

13   15   12

10

P(saw seagull) $= \dfrac{27}{50}$

Page 114 — Sampling and Bias

Q1   E.g. No, Tina can't use her results to draw conclusions about the whole population. The sample is biased because it excludes people who never use the train and most of the people included are likely to use the train regularly. The sample is also too small to represent the whole population.

Page 115 — Collecting Data

Q1   Discrete data

E.g.

Cinema visits	Tally	Frequency
0–9		
10–19		
20–29		
30–39		
40–49		
50 or over		

Page 116 — Mean, Median, Mode and Range

Q1   Mean = 11.2, median = 12, mode = 12, range = 9

Q2   The mean of all 9 heights will be lower than 1.6 m, because the new height is lower than 1.6 m.

Page 117 — Simple Charts and Graphs

Q1 a) 15

b)

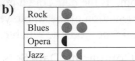

Rock	●
Blues	●●
Opera	◖
Jazz	●◗

Page 118 — Simple Charts and Graphs

Q1 a)

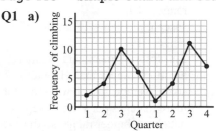

b) 3rd quarter

Page 119 — Pie Charts

Q1

Action 72°   Rom Com

138°

150° Western

Page 120 — Scatter Graphs

Q1 a) There is a strong negative correlation. The longer the run, the slower Sam's speed.

b)

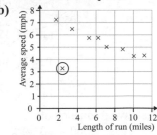

c) Approximately 5 mph (±0.5 mph)

d) The estimate should be reliable because **[either]** 8 miles is within the range of the known data **[or]** the graph shows strong correlation.

Page 121 — Frequency Tables — Finding Averages

Q1 a) Median = 2   **b)** Mean = 1.66

Page 122 — Grouped Frequency Tables

Q1 a) $17.5 \le l < 18.5$

b) 17.4 cm (3 s.f.)

Answers

Page 123 — Interpreting Data

Q1 **a)** 3

b) Probability of selling two pairs
$= \dfrac{10}{50} = \dfrac{1}{5}$ or 0.2.

E.g. the estimate is based on a sample of 50 days, which should be big enough to give a reliable estimate. **[Or]** E.g. The 50 days are consecutive, not picked at random. If the data isn't a good representation of the whole year, the estimate won't be reliable.

Page 124 — Comparing Data Sets

Q1 Hannah: median = 5, mean = 5, range = 10.
Joseph: median = 18, mean = 20, range = 19.
E.g. Joseph's mean and median are much higher than Hannah's, so on average Joseph went to a lot more matches per year. Joseph's data has a bigger range, so the number of matches he attended varied more.

Revision Questions — Section Seven

Q1 $\dfrac{8}{50} = \dfrac{4}{25}$

Q2 0.7

Q3 **a)** HHH, HHT, HTH, THH, TTH, HTT, THT, TTT

b) $\dfrac{3}{8}$

Q4 **a)** See page 109

b) See page 110

Q5 **a)**
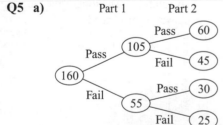

b) Relative frequency of:
pass, pass $= \dfrac{60}{160} = \dfrac{3}{8}$ or 0.375

pass, fail $= \dfrac{45}{160} = \dfrac{9}{32}$ or 0.28125

fail, pass $= \dfrac{30}{160} = \dfrac{3}{16}$ or 0.1875

fail, fail $= \dfrac{25}{160} = \dfrac{5}{32}$ or 0.15625

c) $300 \times 0.375 = 113$ people (to the nearest whole number)

Q6 0.5

Q7
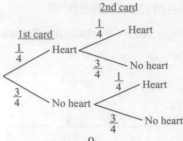

P(no hearts) $= \dfrac{9}{16}$

Q8 **a)**
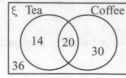

b) $\dfrac{64}{100} = \dfrac{16}{25}$

Q9 A sample is part of a population. Samples need to be representative so that conclusions drawn from sample data can be applied to the whole population.

Q10 Descriptive data

Q11

Pet	Tally	Frequency
Cat	⦀⦀ ⦀⦀⦀	8
Dog	⦀⦀⦀⦀ ⦀	6
Rabbit	⦀⦀⦀⦀	4
Fish	⦀⦀	2

Q12 Mode = 31, Median = 24
Mean = 22, Range = 39

Q13 Count the number of symbols, then use the key to work out what frequency they represent.

Q14 E.g.
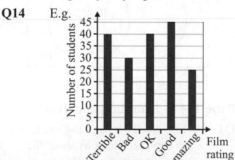
(Or you could draw a pictogram)

Q15 a)
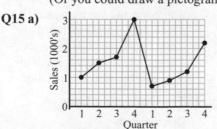

b) There is a seasonal pattern that repeats itself every 4 points. Sales are lowest in the first quarter and highest in the fourth quarter.

Q16 Draw a pie chart to show the proportions.

Q17 a)
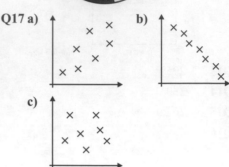
b)

c)

Q18 a) Modal class is: $1.5 \le y < 1.6$.

b) Class containing median is: $1.5 \le y < 1.6$

c) Estimated mean = 1.58 m (to 2 d.p.)

Q19 Outliers can have a big effect on increasing or decreasing the value of the mean or range, so that it doesn't represent the rest of the data set very well.

Q20 Black cars were only owned by men and silver cars were only owned by women. So black cars were more popular amongst men and silver cars were more popular amongst women.
There are similar proportions of men and women owning blue and green cars. So blue and green cars are equally popular amongst men and women.
The proportion of men owning red cars was nearly double the proportion of women owning red cards. So red cars were almost twice as popular amongst men as women.

Index

Index

MFR47 MCFR46 MQFR46 MXFR46